# Glencoe

Volume One, Chapter A
Volume Two, Chapter B

# Algebra 1

Integration
Applications
Connections

# *GLENCOE*

McGraw-Hill

New York, New York   Columbus, Ohio   Woodland Hills, California   Peoria, Illinois

## Glencoe/McGraw-Hill

*A Division of The **McGraw·Hill** Companies*

Send all inquiries to:
Glencoe/McGraw-Hill
8787 Orion Place
Columbus, Ohio  43240

Visit our web page at: http://www.glencoe.com

ISBN: 0-07-822847-6 (Volume One, Student Edition)
ISBN: 0-07-822849-2 (Volume Two, Student Edition)
ISBN: 0-07-822851-4 (Teacher's Annotated Edition)

1 2 3 4 5 6 7 8 9 10 066 03 02 01 00

# Glencoe's Algebra 1 in Two Years!

The ever increasing reliance on technology in our world has led to the need for more students to take algebra and geometry in high school. However, some students have difficulty grasping the abstract concepts of algebra. To aid those students, the Algebra 1 curriculum is often taught over a period of two years. **Glencoe's Algebra 1 in Two Years** is designed for such a program. The extended time frame allows students to spend more time on each concept, which aids their development of in-depth understanding. This also gives students more time to complete hands-on labs and activities that develop these concepts.

The **Algebra 1 in Two Years Resources** is a special package of teaching aids. It includes a Planning Guide, a Block Scheduling Booklet, an Activities Booklet, and a Review and Assessment Booklet for each year. These materials are designed to make it easier for you to effectively teach Algebra 1 in two years.

Also available is the **Teacher's Classroom Resources**. This is a comprehensive package of optional materials that support and extend every lesson. This collection includes 10 different blackline masters booklets, 3 different transparency packages, and 8 other teaching aids. These materials are designed to help you meet the needs of every student.

# Table of Contents

## CHAPTER A

### Prerequisite Concepts

## CHAPTER B

# Components

## Glencoe Algebra 1: Integration, Applications, Connections

| | |
|---|---|
| Volume One, Student Edition | 0-07-822847-6 |
| Volume Two, Student Edition | 0-07-822849-2 |
| Teacher's Wraparound Edition | 0-07-822896-4 |
| Teacher's Annotated Edition, Chapters A and B | 0-07-822851-4 |

| | |
|---|---|
| Algebra 1 in Two Years Resources | 0-02-825343-4 |
| Planning Guide | |
| Block Scheduling Booklet | |
| Activities Booklet | |
| Review and Assessment Booklet | |

**Teacher's Classroom Resources**     0-02-823661-4

*Applications*
Investigations and Projects Masters
Multicultural Activity Masters
Real World Applications Transparencies
Tech Prep Applications Masters
Science and Math Lab Manual
Problem-of-the-Week Cards

*Teaching Aids*
Answer Key Masters
Answer Key Transparencies
Block Scheduling Booklet
Lesson Planning Guide
Solutions Manual
Transparencies A: 5-Minute Check
Transparencies B: Teaching Transparencies

*Meeting Individual Needs*
Enrichment Masters
Practice Masters
Study Guide Masters

*Technology and Multimedia*
Graphing Calculator Masters
Teacher's Guide for Software Resources
Graphing Calculators in the
  Mathematics Classroom

*Assessment and Evaluation*
Assessment and Evaluation Masters
SAT/ACT Study Guide

*Manipulatives and Modeling*
Modeling Mathematics Masters

| | |
|---|---|
| Algebra 1 Spanish Edition | 0-07-823600-2 |
| High School Mathematics Manipulative Kit | 0-02-824847-3 |
| Overhead Manipulative Resources | 0-02-824849-X |
| MindJogger Videoquizzes | 0-02-824891-0 |
| Test and Review Software | |
| Macintosh & Windows | 0-02-824855-4 |
| Interactive Math Tools Software | |
| Macintosh & Windows | 0-02-825345-0 |
| Multimedia Applications CD-ROM | |
| Macintosh & Windows | 0-02-824880-5 |
| Teacher's Handbook | 0-02-824885-6 |

# Pacing Charts

| Year One | | |
|---|---|---|
| **Chapter** | **Days** | |
| | Regular | Block |
| A* | 12 | 6 |
| 1 | 24 | 12 |
| 2 | 26 | 13 |
| 3 | 20 | 10 |
| 4 | 21 | 11 |
| 5 | 23 | 11 |
| 6 | 20 | 10 |
| 7 | 24 | 12 |
| **Total** | **170** | **85** |

| Year Two | | |
|---|---|---|
| **Chapter** | **Days** | |
| | Regular | Block |
| B* | 30 | 17 |
| 7** | 24 | 12 |
| 8 | 17 | 9 |
| 9 | 30 | 13 |
| 10 | 22 | 11 |
| 11 | 20 | 10 |
| 12 | 27 | 13 |
| 13 | 24 | 12 |
| **Total** | **170** | **85** |

* Chapters A and B are optional. See page viii for a description of how to use the pretests and posttests to determine if Chapters A and B are needed.

** Note that if Chapter 7 was covered in Year One, fewer days can be devoted to it.

# How to Use the Pretests and Posttests

The pretests and posttests are designed to help teachers determine whether students are ready to proceed with Algebra 1 in Two Years. Teachers should understand that a student's readiness should not be measured solely using one tool. Teachers may also want to consider factors such as classroom performance and the previous school year's math test scores.

Each test is designed to be completed in 35-40 minutes. All of the tests cover the same basic skills necessary for success in Algebra 1 in Two Years.

Calculator use is not assessed in these tests. Therefore, it is not recommended that students use calculators when taking the tests. Computations required in test items are reasonable, and numbers used in computations are restricted.

The table below gives recommendations for evaluating each test and determining a course of action.

| Action Plan for Chapter A Pretest and Posttest | | |
|---|---|---|
| **Pretest Score** | **Posttest Score** | **Action** |
| 0-14 questions (less than 60%) | 0-14 questions (less than 60%) | Present the prerequisite concepts (pages A6-A29). |
| 15-21 questions (60%-84%) | 15-21 questions (60%-84%) | Review individual concepts as needed. |
| 22-25 questions (88%-100%) | 22-25 questions (88%-100%) | Students are ready to begin the first year of *Algebra 1 in Two Years*. |

| Action Plan for Chapter B Pretest and Posttest | | |
|---|---|---|
| **Pretest Score** | **Posttest Score** | **Action** |
| 0-14 questions (less than 60%) | 0-14 questions (less than 60%) | Present the review lessons and/or chapter tests (pages B4-B56). |
| 15-21 questions (60%-84%) | 15-21 questions (60%-84%) | Review individual lessons as needed. |
| 22-25 questions (88%-100%) | 22-25 questions (88%-100%) | Students are ready to begin the second year of *Algebra 1 in Two Years*. |

# To The Student

Chapter A contains three sections: pretest, concept review, and posttest. The pretest is a mixture of twelve concepts that are generally acknowledged as necessary for success in Algebra 1. You should take the pretest to determine which concepts you need to work on. The concept review section allows you to develop, and eventually master, the individual skills the pretest identified as needing to be reinforced. You should take the posttest to make sure you understand all of the concepts and to measure your progress.

The chart on the next page contains commonly used formulas and measurement conversions. You may use it on the pretest and posttest.

## Formula Chart

| | | |
|---|---|---|
| Perimeter | square<br>rectangle | $P = 4s$<br>$P = 2(\ell + w)$ |
| Circumference | circle | $C = 2\pi r$ |
| Area | square<br>rectangle<br>triangle<br>trapezoid<br>circle | $A = s^2$<br>$A = \ell w$ or $A = bh$<br>$A = \frac{bh}{2}$ or $\frac{1}{2}bh$<br>$A = \frac{1}{2}h(b_1 + b_2)$<br>$A = \pi r^2$ |
| Surface Area | cube<br>cylinder (lateral) | $S = 6s^2$<br>$S = 2\pi rh$ |
| Volume | rectangular prism<br>cylinder<br>cube | $V = \ell wh$<br>$V = \pi r^2 h$<br>$V = s^3$ |
| Pythagorean Theorem | right triangle | $a^2 + b^2 = c^2$ |
| Slope of a Line | $m = \dfrac{y_2 - y_1}{x_2 - x_1}$ | |
| Quadratic Formula | $x = \dfrac{-b \pm \sqrt{b^2 - 4ac}}{2a}$ | |
| Slope-Intercept Form of an Equation | $y = mx + b$ | |
| Point-Slope Form of an Equation | $y - y_1 = m(x - x_1)$ | |
| Standard Form of an Equation | $Ax + By = C$ | |

## Measurement Conversions

| Measure | Metric | Customary |
|---|---|---|
| Length | 1 kilometer = 1000 meters<br>1 meter = 100 centimeters<br>1 centimeter = 10 millimeters | 1 mile = 1760 yards<br>1 mile = 5280 feet<br>1 yard = 3 feet<br>1 foot = 12 inches |
| Volume and Capacity | 1 liter = 1000 milliliters | 1 gallon = 4 quarts<br>1 gallon = 128 ounces<br>1 quart = 2 pints<br>1 pint = 2 cups<br>1 cup = 8 ounces |
| Weight and Mass | 1 kilogram = 1000 grams<br>1 gram = 1000 milligrams | 1 ton = 2000 pounds<br>1 pound = 16 ounces |
| Time | | 1 year = 12 months<br>1 year = 52 weeks<br>1 year = 365 days<br>1 week = 7 days<br>1 day = 24 hours<br>1 hour = 60 minutes<br>1 minute = 60 seconds |

1. The graph below shows the percent of responses in a survey of families in the United States that say they depend on teens to earn money. If 750 people were surveyed, how many of the responses were "Not at all"?  **D**

**Dependent On Teen's Income?**

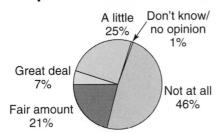

A little 25%
Don't know/ no opinion 1%
Great deal 7%
Fair amount 21%
Not at all 46%

A 5

B 75

C 157.5

D 345

E Not Here

2. The graph below shows a store's monthly sales of CDs.  **F**

**CD Sales**

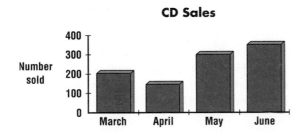

The average price of a CD was $12. What would be a reasonable sales total, with tax, for the CDs sold during the 4-month period?

F More than $12,000

G Between $9600 and $12,000

H Between $7200 and $9600

J Between $4800 and $7200

K Less than $4800

3. The graph below shows the percent of men and women who held two jobs from 1970 to 1995.

**Working Twice a Day**

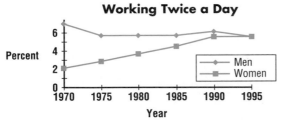

Men
Women

*(Continued at top of next column.)*

Which is a reasonable conclusion from the information on the graph?  **E**

A The number of women working two jobs increases as the number of men working two jobs decreases.

B The number of women working two jobs will continue to increase due to inflation.

C Men are retiring.

D Women are more ambitious.

E The number of men and women working two jobs was the same in 1995.

4. Akikta is making banana bread. The recipe for one loaf calls for $1\frac{3}{4}$ cups of flour. How many cups of flour does he need to make 3 loaves?  **J**

F $4\frac{1}{2}$ c

G $4\frac{3}{4}$ c

H $4\frac{9}{16}$ c

J $5\frac{1}{4}$ c

K Not Here

5. Jorge laid 18 bricks end to end to make a border for a flower bed. Each brick is $8\frac{1}{2}$ inches long. How long is the row of bricks?  **B**

A $26\frac{1}{2}$ in.

B 153 in.

C $144\frac{1}{2}$ in.

D $9\frac{1}{2}$ in.

E Not Here

6. If a bookshelf is 28 inches wide, how many books each $1\frac{3}{4}$ inches wide can be used to fill the shelf?  **J**

F 49

G 36

H 21

J 16

K Not Here

7. A developer has $43\frac{1}{2}$ acres of land that she plans to sell in $\frac{3}{8}$-acre lots. How many lots can she get from this land?  **C**

   A  16.3125

   B  87

   C  116

   D  174

   E  Not Here

8. A recipe calls for $\frac{3}{8}$ cup of milk and $\frac{3}{8}$ cup of syrup. What is the total amount of milk and syrup in the recipe?  **G**

   F  $\frac{3}{8}$ c

   G  $\frac{3}{4}$ c

   H  $1\frac{1}{8}$ c

   J  $\frac{9}{64}$ c

   K  Not Here

9. The width of a column of a magazine is $5\frac{7}{8}$ inches. The left margin is $\frac{7}{8}$ inches, and the right margin is $1\frac{1}{2}$ inches. What is the total width of the page?  **C**

   A  $6\frac{3}{4}$ in.

   B  $7\frac{3}{4}$ in.

   C  $8\frac{1}{4}$ in.

   D  $8\frac{1}{8}$ in.

   E  Not Here

10. Mr. Baker had $5\frac{1}{2}$ yards of curtain material. He used $2\frac{7}{8}$ yards. How much material did he have left?  **J**

   F  $8\frac{3}{8}$ yd

   G  $7\frac{3}{8}$ yd

   H  $3\frac{5}{8}$ yd

   J  $2\frac{5}{8}$ yd

   K  Not Here

11. Jane and Julie are identical twins. At birth, Jane weighed $5\frac{5}{8}$ pounds, and Julie weighed 7 pounds. What was the difference in their weight?  **E**

   A  $\frac{3}{4}$ lb

   B  $1\frac{1}{4}$ lb

   C  $2\frac{1}{8}$ lb

   D  $2\frac{3}{4}$ lb

   E  Not Here

12. What is the approximate width of a door?  **F**

   F  1.2 meters

   G  12 centimeters

   H  12 millimeters

   J  1.2 millimeters

13. Ken's recipe for chili calls for $3\frac{1}{2}$ cups of tomato sauce. He pours two 14-ounce cans of tomato sauce into a pan. How many more *ounces* does Ken need to add?  **A**

   A  0 oz.

   B  4 oz.

   C  6 oz.

   D  8 oz.

   E  Not Here

14. Light travels approximately 1.86 million miles in 10 seconds. The distance from the sun to Earth is about 93 million miles. Which proportion could be used to find $x$, the time it takes for light to travel from the sun to Earth?  **K**

   F  $\frac{1.86}{x} = \frac{93}{10}$

   G  $\frac{1.86}{10} = \frac{x}{93}$

   H  $\frac{1.0}{x} = \frac{93}{1.86}$

   J  $\frac{1.0}{93} = \frac{x}{1.86}$

   K  $\frac{1.86}{10} = \frac{93}{x}$

**15.** The ratio of your weight on the moon to your weight on Earth is about 1:6. If you weigh 72 kilograms on Earth, about how much would you weigh on the moon? **D**

   **A** 36 kg

   **B** 28 kg

   **C** 14 kg

   **D** 12 kg

   **E** Not Here

**16.** In the figure below, what is the total number of rays in which the endpoint is *P*? **J**

   **F** 1

   **G** 2

   **H** 3

   **J** 4

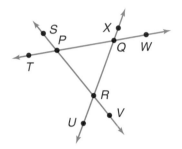

**17.** The sides of the triangle are best described as: **B**

   **A** rays

   **B** line segments

   **C** angles

   **D** lines

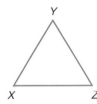

**18.** Tashema wants to frame a rectangular picture that is 12 inches by 18 inches. What is the perimeter in *feet*? **H**

   **F** 60 ft          **H** 5 ft

   **G** 24 ft          **J** $2\frac{1}{2}$ ft

**19.** The area of a basketball court is 4032 square feet. If the length of the court is 84 feet, what is the *approximate* width of the court? **B**

   **A** 40 ft          **C** 80 ft

   **B** 50 ft          **D** 90 ft

**20.** What is the surface area of the prism? **G**

   **E** 31.5 sq cm

   **F** 297 sq cm

   **G** 316 sq cm

   **H** 346.5 sq cm

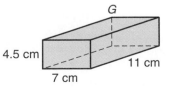

**21.** What is the volume of the cylinder? $\left(\text{Use } \pi \approx \frac{22}{7}.\right)$ **C**

   **A** 88 in$^3$

   **B** 176 in$^3$

   **C** $276\frac{4}{7}$ in$^3$

   **D** 352 in$^3$

   **E** Not Here

**22.** Jamonte hikes 6 kilometers north and then 8 kilometers west. How far is he from his starting point? **F**

   **F** 10 km

   **G** 12 km

   **H** 14 km

   **J** 100 km

**23.** *ABCD* is a rectangle. *AD* = 7 centimeters and *AC* = 25 centimeters. What is the length of $\overline{CD}$? 

   **A** 576 cm

   **B** 175 cm

   **C** 64 cm

   **D** 32 cm

   **E** 24 cm          **E**

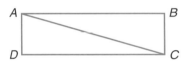

**24.** The school store has sweatshirts in 4 sizes and in 3 different colors. If the store has one of every possible size and color sweatshirt, how many different sweatshirts do they have? **H**

   **F** 7

   **G** 8

   **H** 12

   **J** 14

**25.** If a fair coin is tossed 4 times, the probability that 4 heads will occur is $\frac{1}{16}$. What is the probability that 4 heads will *not* occur? **C**

   **A** $\frac{7}{8}$

   **B** $\frac{1}{16}$

   **C** $\frac{15}{16}$

   **D** $\frac{3}{4}$

# Statistics: Graphs

**WhaT YOU'LL LEARN**

- To interpret graphs in real-world settings.

**Why IT'S IMPORTANT**

Graphs are a useful way to display data so it can be understood quickly and easily.

When data is collected and displayed in a graph, you can look for trends and often make decisions or predictions based on the data.

The most common statistical graphs include *line graphs*, *circle graphs*, and *bar graphs*. A **line graph** is the usual choice to show how values change over a period of time.

**Example** **1** The double-line graph at the right shows the percent of young people who go out on dates and who play pickup sports games.

a. At what age does dating become as popular as sports?

b. What is the percent of young people who date and play pickup sports when both are equally popular?

**Ready, Set, Shift**

**Source:** Youth Sports Institute, Michigan

a. By looking at the graph, you can see that the lines appear to intersect at or shortly after 12 years of age. This is the age where dating becomes as popular as sports.

b. about 35%

Circle graphs may be the most popular type of visual display of data because they allow for more creativity than the other types. Circle graphs are used to show how parts are related to the whole.

**Example** **2** The graph below shows how people describe their health. If 1500 people were surveyed to determine the graph, how many people responded good or very good?

Look at the section representing responses of good and very good.

A total of 29.9% + 36.1% or 66% responded good or very good. Find 66% of 1500 to find the number of people surveyed who answered good or very good.

1500 × .66 = 990

990 people responded good or very good.

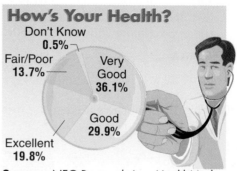

**How's Your Health?**

- Don't Know 0.5%
- Fair/Poor 13.7%
- Very Good 36.1%
- Good 29.9%
- Excellent 19.8%

**Source:** NFO Research, Inc., HealthMed Division

A **bar graph** is used to compare quantities.

**Example ③** The double-bar graph at the right shows how long men and women think it will be before a woman is elected U.S. president.

a. **During which time interval is the difference between men and women the greatest?**

b. **What is the size of this gap?**

a. By looking at the graph, the greatest gap between men and women is in the interval labeled 11–20 years.

b. The gap is 35% − 28% or 7%.

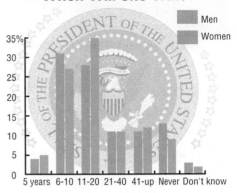

**When Will She Win?**

Men
Women

5 years  6-10  11-20  21-40  41-up  Never  Don't know

**Source:** Yankelovich for Gazelle Productions

## EXERCISES

**Practice**

1. line graph to show how values changed over time

2. bar graph to compare quantities

3. circle graph to show how parts relate to the whole

4. double-bar graph comparing quantities; or double-line graph to show how values changed over time

5. circle graph to show how parts relate to the whole

**For each set of data, determine whether a bar graph, circle graph, or line graph is the best way to display the data.**

1. number of viewers of football on Monday night each year from 1970 to 1996

2. how much different age groups in the U.S. spend on sporting apparel

3. how U.S. consumers pay for goods and services

4. the percent of men and women who held two jobs from 1977 to 1996

5. the publishing budget for your school yearbook

6. number of U.S. shipments of CDs and cassette tapes from 1985 to 1994

**Solve. Use the line graph.**

7. About how many more women ran for congress in 1992 than in 1988?

8. In what two-year span did the largest increase in the number of female candidates running for congress occur? **between 1990 and 1992**

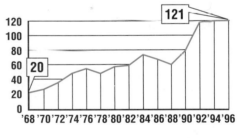

**Female Candidates for U.S. Congress**

121

20

'68 '70 '72 '74 '76 '78 '80 '82 '84 '86 '88 '90 '92 '94 '96

**Applications**

6. double-bar graph comparing quantities; or double-line graph to show how values changed over time

7. 60 women

9–10. See Teacher's Answer Key.

**Draw a graph that you might use to accurately represent the data. You may want to use computer software.**

9. **Olympics** The table at the right shows the number of gold medals earned by athletes from the United States in the six summer Olympic Games from 1976 to 1996.

10. **Advertising** The table at the right shows what TV viewers did when a commercial came on in 1985 and in 1991.

| Year | Gold Medals |
|------|-------------|
| 1976 | 34 |
| 1980 | 0 |
| 1984 | 83 |
| 1988 | 36 |
| 1992 | 37 |
| 1996 | 44 |

| Activity | 1985 | 1991 |
|----------|------|------|
| Change channel/mute | 13% | 22% |
| Stop paying attention | 25% | 27% |
| Watch the commercial | 33% | 33% |
| Leave the room or do something else | 29% | 18% |

# Multiplying Fractions and Mixed Numbers

You can draw an **area model** on grid paper to show multiplication of fractions. The diagram at the right models the product $\frac{2}{3} \cdot \frac{3}{4}$. The rectangle is three units wide. Two columns are colored yellow to represent $\frac{2}{3}$. The rectangle is four units long. Three rows are colored blue to represent $\frac{3}{4}$. Notice that twelve 1-by-1 squares are inside the rectangle and six of them overlap the blue and yellow, which results in green. The product of $\frac{2}{3}$ and $\frac{3}{4}$ is $\frac{6}{12}$, or $\frac{1}{2}$.

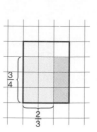

An area model shows what happens when you multiply fractions. You will get the same results if you multiply fractions as shown below.

$$\frac{2}{3} \cdot \frac{3}{4} = \frac{2 \cdot 3}{3 \cdot 4} \quad \textit{Multiply the numerators and multiply the denominators.}$$

$$= \frac{6}{12} \text{ or } \frac{1}{2} \quad \textit{Simplify by dividing the numerator and denominator by 6.}$$

| **Multiplying Fractions and Mixed Numbers** | **To multiply fractions, multiply the numerators and then multiply the denominators. Simplify if necessary.** |
|---|---|
| | **To multiply mixed numbers, rename each mixed number as an improper fraction. Multiply the fractions.** |

You can use the following shortcut to simplify a product.

$$\frac{3}{4} \cdot \frac{8}{9} = \frac{3 \cdot 8}{4 \cdot 9} \quad \textit{Divide both the numerator and the denominator by 3 and 4.}$$

$$= \frac{\overset{1}{\cancel{3}} \cdot \overset{2}{\cancel{8}}}{\underset{1}{\cancel{4}} \cdot \underset{3}{\cancel{9}}} \quad \begin{array}{l}\textit{3 is the greatest common factor (GCF) of 3 and 9.}\\ \textit{4 is the GCF of 4 and 8.}\end{array}$$

$$= \frac{2}{3} \quad \leftarrow \textit{simplest form}$$

**Example** ① Solve $x = \frac{1}{3} \cdot 5\frac{1}{4}$.

$$x = \frac{1}{3} \cdot 5\frac{1}{4}$$

$$x = \frac{1}{3} \cdot \frac{21}{4} \quad \textit{Rename } 5\frac{1}{4} \textit{ as } \frac{21}{4}.$$

$$x = \frac{1 \cdot \overset{7}{\cancel{21}}}{\underset{1}{\cancel{3}} \cdot 4} \quad \begin{array}{l}\textit{The GCF of 21 and 3 is 3.}\\ \textit{Divide 21 and 3 by 3.}\end{array}$$

$$x = \frac{7}{4} \text{ or } 1\frac{3}{4}$$

**Practice**

**1. Draw** an area model that demonstrates that the product of $\frac{3}{4}$ and $\frac{1}{2}$ is $\frac{3}{8}$.

**1.**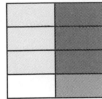

**Solve each equation. Write the solution in simplest form.**

**2.** $\frac{1}{7}\left(\frac{1}{3}\right) = x$   $\frac{1}{21}$

**3.** $v = \frac{2}{3}\left(\frac{1}{5}\right)$   $\frac{2}{15}$

**4.** $\frac{5}{6}\left(\frac{3}{10}\right) = y$   $\frac{1}{4}$

**5.** $w = \frac{7}{12}\left(\frac{4}{5}\right)$   $\frac{7}{15}$

**6.** $\frac{7}{10}\left(\frac{5}{28}\right) = z$   $\frac{1}{8}$

**7.** $s = \frac{9}{15}\left(\frac{5}{9}\right)$   $\frac{1}{3}$

**8.** What is the product of 9 and $\frac{2}{3}$?   **6**

**9.** What is $\frac{4}{5}$ of 30?   **24**

**10.** What is $\frac{2}{5}$ of $10\frac{1}{2}$?   **$4\frac{1}{5}$**

**Solve each equation. Write the solution in simplest form.**

**11.** $k = 2\left(1\frac{5}{18}\right)$   **$2\frac{5}{9}$**

**12.** $3\frac{2}{5}(10) = m$   **34**

**13.** $n = 2\left(3\frac{5}{8}\right)$   **$7\frac{1}{4}$**

**14.** $2\frac{2}{3}\left(\frac{4}{5}\right) = n$   **$2\frac{2}{15}$**

**15.** $t = \frac{7}{8}\left(4\frac{1}{4}\right)$   **$3\frac{23}{32}$**

**16.** $d = 2\frac{3}{10}\left(\frac{5}{12}\right)$   **$\frac{23}{24}$**

**17.** $9\frac{1}{3}\left(3\frac{3}{4}\right) = f$   **35**

**18.** $3\frac{1}{3}\left(4\frac{1}{2}\right) = w$   **15**

**19.** $v = 6\frac{1}{4}\left(1\frac{7}{16}\right)$   **$8\frac{63}{64}$**

**20.** $\left(1\frac{7}{8}\right)4\frac{2}{7}\left(3\frac{4}{8}\right) = c$   **$28\frac{1}{8}$**

**21.** $3\frac{1}{8}\left(2\frac{4}{5}\right)\left(\frac{5}{7}\right) = p$   **$6\frac{1}{4}$**

**22.** $3\frac{2}{3}\left(\frac{1}{8}\right)\left(1\frac{1}{11}\right) = h$   **$\frac{1}{2}$**

**Applications**

**23. Statistics**   The graph at the right shows which fast-food restaurants kids prefer according to a 1995 poll. Suppose 600 kids participated in the survey.

a. How many kids preferred Restaurant B?   **78 kids**

b. How many kids preferred Restaurant D?   **24 kids**

c. How many more kids preferred Restaurant A over Restaurant C?   **198 kids**

### Kid's Fast-Food Favorites

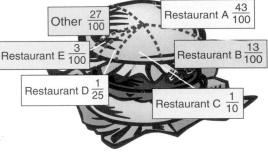

Other $\frac{27}{100}$

Restaurant A $\frac{43}{100}$

Restaurant E $\frac{3}{100}$

Restaurant B $\frac{13}{100}$

Restaurant D $\frac{1}{25}$

Restaurant C $\frac{1}{10}$

**24. Economics**   The sales tax in Franklin County is $7\frac{3}{4}$%. This means for every dollar you spend, you pay $7\frac{3}{4}$¢ in tax. If you purchase an item for $24, how much will you owe in tax?   **$1.86**

**25. Economics**   A personal AM/FM radio and cassette player that usually sells for $69 is on sale at $\frac{1}{3}$ off. This means that it is on sale for $\frac{2}{3}$ of the regular price. What is the sale price?   **$46**

# Dividing Fractions and Mixed Numbers

## *What* YOU'LL LEARN

- To divide fractions and mixed numbers.

## *Why* IT'S IMPORTANT

You can divide fractions to help you solve problems involving home economics and carpentry.

Dana is planning a pizza party. She estimates that each person will eat an average of $\frac{2}{3}$ of a pizza. If she buys four pizzas, will there be enough for five people?

To solve this problem, you need to find how many $\frac{2}{3}$ pizzas are in 4 pizzas.

### Method 1

You can model the problem above using an area model. Divide 4 by $\frac{2}{3}$.

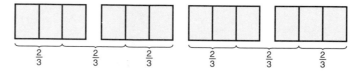

So, $4 \div \frac{2}{3} = 6$.

### Method 2

You can also divide by a fraction or mixed number. To do this, multiply by its multiplicative inverse.

$$4 \div \frac{2}{3} = \frac{4}{1} \div \frac{2}{3} \quad \text{\itshape Rename 4 as } \frac{4}{1}.$$

$$= \frac{4}{1} \cdot \frac{3}{2} \quad \text{\itshape Dividing by } \frac{2}{3} \text{ is the same as multiplying by } \frac{3}{2}.$$

$$= \frac{12}{2} \text{ or } 6$$

Four pizzas will be enough to feed 6 people.

*You can also use the GCF of 2 and 4, which is 2.*

$$4 \div \frac{2}{3} = \frac{\overset{2}{\cancel{4}}}{1} \cdot \frac{3}{\underset{1}{\cancel{2}}}$$

$$= \frac{6}{1} \text{ or } 6$$

---

| **Dividing Fractions and Mixed Numbers** | **To divide by a fraction, multiply by its multiplicative inverse. Simplify if necessary.** <br><br> **To divide by a mixed number, rename the mixed number as an improper fraction. Multiply by its multiplicative inverse.** |
|---|---|

**Example** **1** Solve $x = \frac{2}{3} \div 2\frac{6}{7}$.

$$x = \frac{2}{3} \div 2\frac{6}{7}$$

$$x = \frac{2}{3} \div \frac{20}{7} \quad \text{\itshape Rename } 2\frac{6}{7} \text{ as } \frac{20}{7}.$$

$$x = \frac{2}{3} \cdot \frac{7}{20} \quad \text{\itshape Dividing by } \frac{20}{7} \text{ is the same as multiplying by } \frac{7}{20}.$$

$$x = \frac{\overset{1}{\cancel{2}} \cdot 7}{3 \cdot \underset{10}{\cancel{20}}} \quad \text{\itshape The GCF of 2 and 20 is 2. Divide 2 and 20 by 2.}$$

$$x = \frac{7}{30}$$

**Practice**

1.

| $\frac{1}{2}$ | | | | | |
|---|---|---|---|---|---|
| $\frac{1}{12}$ | $\frac{1}{12}$ | $\frac{1}{12}$ | $\frac{1}{12}$ | $\frac{1}{12}$ | $\frac{1}{12}$ |

1. **Draw** an area model that demonstrates $\frac{1}{2} \div 6 = \frac{1}{12}$.
**See Teacher's Answer Key.**

**Solve each equation. Write the solution in simplest form.**

2. $2 \div \frac{1}{3} = j$  **6**

3. $g = \frac{1}{2} \div 8$  **$\frac{1}{16}$**

4. $3 \div \frac{1}{2} = y$  **6**

5. $q = 7 \div 4$  **$1\frac{3}{4}$**

6. $n = 5 \div 11$  **$\frac{5}{11}$**

7. $\frac{5}{6} \div \frac{1}{6} = f$  **5**

8. What is the quotient of $\frac{2}{3}$ and $\frac{4}{9}$?  **$1\frac{1}{2}$**

9. Solve the equation $c = \left(\frac{1}{4} \cdot \frac{5}{8}\right) \div 3\frac{1}{5}$.  **$\frac{25}{512}$**

**Solve each equation. Write the solution in simplest form.**

10. $r = \frac{7}{9} \div \frac{1}{9}$  **7**

11. $\frac{7}{16} \div \frac{7}{11} = s$  **$\frac{11}{6}$**

12. $\frac{6}{13} \div \frac{5}{7} = t$  **$\frac{42}{65}$**

13. $e = 1\frac{3}{4} \div \frac{7}{12}$  **3**

14. $f = \frac{3}{5} \div 11\frac{2}{5}$  **$\frac{1}{19}$**

15. $4\frac{2}{5} \div \frac{11}{15} = g$  **6**

16. $d = 1 \div 2\frac{3}{5}$  **$\frac{5}{13}$**

17. $2\frac{5}{8} \div 7\frac{1}{2} = x$  **$\frac{7}{20}$**

18. $5\frac{3}{5} \div 4\frac{1}{5} = y$  **$1\frac{1}{3}$**

**Applications**

19. **Carpentry**  Builders Square has two stacks of $\frac{5}{8}$-in. plywood sheets. One stack is 40 inches high. The other is 25 inches high. How many sheets of plywood are there in both stacks?  **104 sheets**

20. **Home Economics**  The graph below shows the cost per year for different uses of energy in the average household.

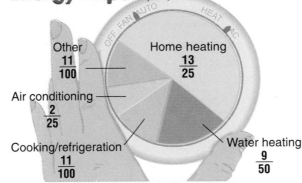

**Source:** *The Family Handyman,* Reader's Digest Special Interest Magazine Group

a. Suppose a family's only use of natural gas is for water heating. If their cost for gas in a year is $172.80, what was their total household energy expense for the year?  **$960**

b. How many times as much does it cost for water heating than it does for air conditioning?  **$\frac{9}{4}$ times**

c. How many times as much does it cost for heating the home than it does for air conditioning?  **$6\frac{1}{2}$ times**

# Adding Fractions and Mixed Numbers

**What YOU'LL LEARN**

- To add fractions and mixed numbers.

**Why IT'S IMPORTANT**

You can divide fractions to help you solve problems involving cooking, carpentry, and consumer spending.

Since a fraction can be represented using an area model, you can model the addition of fractions by using different colors of shading. The model at the right represents $\frac{3}{5} + \frac{1}{5}$. Since 4 of the 5 sections are shaded, the sum is $\frac{4}{5}$.

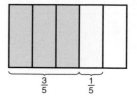

| Adding Like Fractions | To add fractions with like denominators, add the numerators. Then simplify. |
|---|---|

**Example** **1** Solve each equation. Write the solution in simplest form.

a. $\frac{2}{3} + \frac{2}{3} = x$

$\quad\quad \frac{4}{3} = x$   *Since the denominators are the same, add the numerators.*

$\quad\quad 1\frac{1}{3} = x$   *Rename $\frac{4}{3}$ as a mixed number.*

b. $t = 2\frac{3}{8} + 3\frac{5}{8}$

$\quad t = (2 + 3) + \left(\frac{3}{8} + \frac{5}{8}\right)$   *Use the associative and commutative properties to add the whole numbers and fractions separately.*

$\quad t = 5 + \frac{8}{8}$   *Add the numerators of the fractions.*

$\quad t = 5 + 1 \text{ or } 6$   *Simplify.*

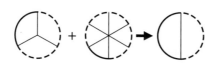

The model at the left represents the sum of $\frac{1}{3}$ and $\frac{1}{6}$. This leads us to the following rule for adding unlike fractions.

| Adding Unlike Fractions | To find the sum of two fractions with unlike denominators, rename the fractions with a common denominator. Then add and simplify. |
|---|---|

**Example** **2** Solve each equation. Write the solution in simplest form.

a. $y = \frac{1}{8} + \frac{3}{4}$   *The least common multiple (LCM) of 8 and 4 is 8.*

$\quad y = \frac{1}{8} + \frac{6}{8}$   *Rename $\frac{3}{4}$ as $\frac{6}{8}$.*

$\quad y = \frac{7}{8}$

**b.** $9\frac{1}{6} + 7\frac{7}{9} = d$  *Use the LCM of 6 and 9 to rename $\frac{1}{6}$ as $\frac{3}{18}$ and $\frac{7}{9}$ as $\frac{14}{18}$.*

$\quad 9\frac{3}{18} + 7\frac{14}{18} = d$

$\quad\quad 16\frac{17}{18} = d$  *Add the whole numbers. Then add the fractions.*

## EXERCISES

**Practice**

**Write the addition sentence shown by each model.**   2. $\frac{1}{2} + \frac{1}{6} = \frac{2}{3}$

1. $\frac{3}{4} + \frac{3}{4} = 1\frac{1}{2}$

1.

**Draw an area model to show each sum.**

3.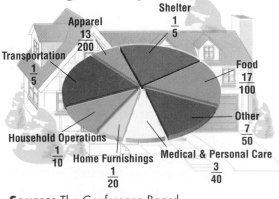

3. $\frac{5}{8} + \frac{5}{8} = 1\frac{1}{4}$

4. $\frac{1}{2} + \frac{1}{4} = \frac{3}{4}$

4.

**Solve each equation. Write each solution in simplest form.**

5. $x = \frac{1}{3} + \frac{1}{3}$   $\frac{2}{3}$

6. $\frac{4}{7} + \frac{5}{7} = a$   $1\frac{2}{7}$

7. $\frac{2}{9} + \frac{4}{9} = t$   $\frac{2}{3}$

8. $y = \frac{1}{8} + \frac{3}{8}$   $\frac{1}{2}$

9. $\frac{1}{6} + \frac{5}{6} = f$   $1$

10. $\frac{7}{12} + \frac{11}{12} = g$   $1\frac{1}{2}$

11. $\frac{1}{3} + \frac{1}{2} = b$   $\frac{5}{6}$

12. $r = \frac{1}{2} + \frac{1}{8}$   $\frac{5}{8}$

13. $h = \frac{2}{3} + \frac{3}{4}$   $1\frac{5}{12}$

14. $\frac{1}{2} + \frac{1}{8} + \frac{1}{4} = z$   $\frac{7}{8}$

15. $c = \frac{7}{8} + \frac{3}{4} + \frac{1}{2}$   $2\frac{1}{8}$

16. $m = \frac{1}{4} + \frac{1}{3} + \frac{1}{2}$   $1\frac{1}{12}$

17. $4\frac{1}{2} + \frac{5}{8} = k$   $5\frac{1}{8}$

18. $s = 73\frac{1}{2} + \frac{2}{3}$   $74\frac{1}{6}$

19. $3\frac{1}{4} + 5\frac{1}{3} = d$   $8\frac{7}{12}$

20. $j = 9\frac{1}{3} + 5\frac{5}{6}$   $15\frac{1}{6}$

21. $v = 4\frac{1}{2} + 7\frac{5}{8}$   $12\frac{1}{8}$

22. $1\frac{2}{3} + 5\frac{7}{8} = n$   $7\frac{13}{24}$

**Applications**

23. $\frac{7}{12}$ cup

24. $\frac{3}{4}$ inch

23. **Home Economics**   Mr. Sopher used $\frac{1}{3}$ cup of sour cream and $\frac{1}{4}$ cup of mayonnaise as the base for a dip. How much dip does he have so far?

24. **Carpentry**   The students in Advanced Cabinetry made a desktop by gluing a sheet of $\frac{1}{16}$-inch walnut veneer to both sides of a sheet of $\frac{5}{8}$-inch plywood. What was the total thickness of the desktop?

25. **Consumer Spending**
The graph at the right shows the fraction of each dollar a family spends on different expenses.

a. What fraction of each dollar is spent on shelter and transportation?

b. What fraction of each dollar is spent on apparel and medical/personal care?

c. What fraction of each dollar is spent on things not mentioned in parts a and b?

25a. $\frac{2}{5}$

25b. $\frac{7}{50}$

25c. $\frac{23}{50}$

**Average Family Budget, 1990**

Shelter $\frac{1}{5}$

Apparel $\frac{13}{200}$

Transportation $\frac{1}{5}$

Food $\frac{17}{100}$

Other $\frac{7}{50}$

Household Operations $\frac{1}{10}$

Home Furnishings $\frac{1}{20}$

Medical & Personal Care $\frac{3}{40}$

**Source:** The Conference Board

*Adding Fractions and Mixed Numbers*   **A13**

# Subtracting Fractions and Mixed Numbers

**What YOU'LL LEARN**

- To subtract fractions and mixed numbers.

**Why IT'S IMPORTANT**

You can subtract fractions to help you solve problems involving sewing and business.

As you can see in the model below, subtracting fractions with like denominators is similar to adding fractions with like denominators. The model represents $\frac{3}{4} - \frac{1}{4}$. Since 2 of the 4 sections are shaded, the difference is $\frac{2}{4}$ or $\frac{1}{2}$.

| Subtracting Like Fractions | To subtract fractions with like denominators, subtract the numerators. Then simplify. |
|---|---|

**Example** **1** Solve each equation. Write the solution in simplest form.

a. $\frac{3}{5} - \frac{1}{5} = m$

$\quad \frac{2}{5} = m$   *Since the denominators are the same, subtract the numerators.*

b. $n = 4\frac{1}{8} - 2\frac{5}{8}$

$\quad n = 3\frac{9}{8} - 2\frac{5}{8}$   *Replace $4\frac{1}{8}$ with $3\frac{9}{8}$.*

$\quad n = (3 - 2) + \left(\frac{9}{8} - \frac{5}{8}\right)$   *Use the associative and commutative properties to subtract the whole numbers and fractions separately.*

$\quad n = 1 + \frac{4}{8}$   *Subtract the numerators of the fractions.*

$\quad n = 1 + \frac{1}{2}$ or $1\frac{1}{2}$   *Simplify.*

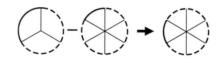

The model at the left represents the difference of $\frac{1}{3}$ and $\frac{1}{6}$. This leads us to the following rule for subtracting unlike fractions.

| Subtracting Unlike Fractions | To find the difference of two fractions with unlike denominators, rename the fractions with a common denominator. Then subtract and simplify. |
|---|---|

**Example** **2** Solve each equation. Write the solution in simplest form.

a. $p = \frac{6}{7} - \frac{2}{3}$

$\quad p = \frac{18}{21} - \frac{14}{21}$   *The LCM of 7 and 3 is 21. Rename $\frac{6}{7}$ as $\frac{18}{21}$ and $\frac{2}{3}$ as $\frac{14}{21}$.*

$\quad p = \frac{4}{21}$

**b.** $9\frac{1}{6} - 7\frac{7}{9} = q$

$\phantom{.}9\frac{3}{18} - 7\frac{14}{18} = q$    *Use the LCM of 6 and 9 to rename $\frac{1}{6}$ as $\frac{3}{18}$ and $\frac{7}{9}$ as $\frac{14}{18}$.*

$8\frac{21}{18} - 7\frac{14}{18} = q$    *Rename $9\frac{3}{18}$ as $8\frac{21}{18}$.*

$\phantom{8\frac{21}{18}-}1\frac{7}{18} = q$    *Subtract the whole numbers. Then subtract the fractions.*

## EXERCISES

**Practice**

**Write the subtraction sentence shown by each model.**

1. $\frac{7}{8} - \frac{5}{8} = \frac{1}{4}$

2. $\frac{2}{3} - \frac{1}{2} = \frac{1}{6}$

1.

2.

**Draw an area model to show each difference.**

3.

3. $\frac{3}{5} - \frac{2}{5} = \frac{1}{5}$

4. $\frac{1}{2} - \frac{1}{4} = \frac{1}{4}$

4.

**Solve each equation. Write the solution in simplest form.**

5. $\frac{5}{8} - \frac{1}{8} = w$   $\frac{1}{2}$

6. $\frac{5}{6} - \frac{1}{6} = p$   $\frac{2}{3}$

7. $\frac{9}{10} - \frac{7}{10} = n$   $\frac{1}{5}$

8. $u = \frac{7}{11} - \frac{3}{11}$   $\frac{4}{11}$

9. $1\frac{1}{4} - \frac{3}{4} = g$   $\frac{1}{2}$

10. $x = \frac{7}{12} - \frac{1}{12}$   $\frac{1}{2}$

11. $\frac{1}{2} - \frac{1}{8} = j$   $\frac{3}{8}$

12. $\frac{2}{3} - \frac{1}{6} = m$   $\frac{1}{2}$

13. $k = \frac{5}{6} - \frac{5}{12}$   $\frac{5}{12}$

14. $\frac{1}{2} - \frac{1}{3} = v$   $\frac{1}{6}$

15. $\frac{5}{6} - \frac{3}{4} = d$   $\frac{1}{12}$

16. $b = \frac{8}{9} - \frac{1}{6}$   $\frac{13}{18}$

17. $z = 7\frac{5}{8} - 4\frac{5}{8}$   $3$

18. $c = 15 - 2\frac{1}{3}$   $12\frac{2}{3}$

19. $f = 4\frac{5}{8} - 3\frac{1}{2}$   $1\frac{1}{8}$

20. $8\frac{7}{8} - 4\frac{2}{3} = r$   $4\frac{5}{24}$

21. $4\frac{1}{2} - 2\frac{3}{4} = q$   $1\frac{3}{4}$

22. $h = 5\frac{5}{16} - 2\frac{3}{8}$   $2\frac{15}{16}$

23. Subtract $\frac{11}{16}$ from 20.   $19\frac{5}{16}$

**Applications**

24. **Sewing** Becky is making a suit. She needs $2\frac{5}{8}$ yards of material for the jacket and $\frac{7}{8}$ yard of material for the skirt. How much more material does she need for the jacket than the skirt?   **$1\frac{3}{4}$ yards**

25. **Business** The chart at the right shows the closing price of Kein stock for each day of the week before the 1996 New York City Marathon.

   **a.** How much did the price of the stock drop from Tuesday to Wednesday?   **$1\frac{1}{8}$**

   **b.** Between which two consecutive days did the largest drop occur?

   **$4\frac{3}{8}$ between Thursday and Friday**

| Day | Closing Price |
|-----|---------------|
| Monday | $62\frac{1}{4}$ |
| Tuesday | $60\frac{7}{8}$ |
| Wednesday | $59\frac{3}{4}$ |
| Thursday | $59\frac{1}{8}$ |
| Friday | $54\frac{3}{4}$ |

*Subtracting Fractions and Mixed Numbers*   **A15**

# Measurement

**What YOU'LL LEARN**

• To use metric and customary units of measurement.

**Why IT'S IMPORTANT**

You can use measurement in situations involving countries that use the metric system or every day situations like cooking.

The **meter (m)** is the standard unit of length in the metric system. All units of length in the metric system are defined in terms of the meter. In the customary system, the basic unit of length is the **inch (in.)**.

| Metric Length | Customary Length |
|---|---|
| 1000 millimeters (mm) = 1 meter | 12 inches = 1 foot (ft) |
| 100 centimeters (cm) = 1 meter | 3 feet = 1 yard (yd) |
| 1000 meters = 1 kilometer (km) | 1760 yards = 1 mile (mi) |

The **liter (L)** is the standard unit of capacity in the metric system. Liters, milliliters, kiloliters, and so on, are related in a manner similar to the units of length. In the customary system, the basic unit of capacity for liquids is the **fluid ounce (fl oz)**.

| Metric Capacity | Customary Capacity |
|---|---|
| 1000 milliliters (mL) = 1 liter | 8 fluid ounces = 1 cup (c) |
| 1000 liters = 1 kiloliter (kL) | 2 cups = 1 pint (pt) |
|  | 2 pints = 1 quart (qt) |
|  | 4 quarts = 1 gallon (gal) |

The *mass* of an object is the amount of matter that it contains. The **gram (g)** is the standard unit of mass in the metric system. Units of mass are also related in a manner similar to the units of length. In the customary system, the basic unit of *weight* is the **ounce (oz)**.

| Metric Mass | Customary Weight |
|---|---|
| 1000 milligrams (mg) = 1 gram | 16 ounces = 1 pound (lb) |
| 1000 grams = 1 kilogram (kg) | 2000 pounds = 1 ton (T) |

To convert units within the metric system, you follow the same procedure as when you multiply or divide by powers of ten.

*The prefixes in capital letters are more commonly used.*

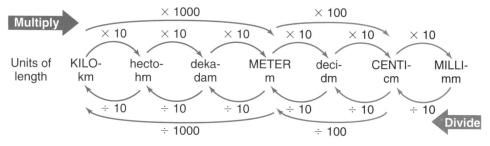

**Example** ❶ Complete each sentence.

a. **200 cm = _?_ m**

Centimeters are smaller than meters. Converting to larger units means there will be fewer units. Divide by 100.

$200 \div 100 = 2$

$200 \text{ cm} = 2 \text{ m}$

b. **0.354 L = _?_ mL**

Liters are larger than milliliters. Converting to smaller units means there will be more units. Multiply by 1000.

$0.354 \times 1000 = 354$

$0.354 \text{ L} = 354 \text{ mL}$

Converting from one unit to another in the customary system may involve more than one step. The rules about when to multiply or divide are the same as those used with the metric system.

**Example** **2** Complete each sentence.

a. **1035 ft = _?_ yd**

Feet are smaller than yards. Smaller to larger means fewer units. Divide by 3 since there are 3 feet in a yard.

$1035 \div 3 = 345$
$1035 \text{ ft} = 345 \text{ yd}$

b. **8 qt = _?_ pt**

Quarts are larger than pints. Larger to smaller means more units. Multiply by 2.

$8 \times 2 = 16$
$8 \text{ qt} = 16 \text{ pt}$

## EXERCISES

**Practice**

1. Suppose your best friend misses school the day measurement was covered. Write a few sentences telling her how to determine when to multiply or divide when converting measures. **Sample answer: Smaller to larger means divide. Larger to smaller means multiply.**

**Complete each sentence.**

2. 6.9 mm = _?_ cm  **0.69**

3. 2.5 km = _?_ m  **2500**

4. 9.1 kg = _?_ mg  **9,100,000**

5. 34 cm = _?_ m  **0.34**

6. 642 mL = _?_ L  **0.642**

7. 7 g = _?_ mg  **7000**

8. 12 ft = _?_ in.  **144**

9. 4 T = _?_ lb  **8000**

10. 9 pt = _?_ c  **18**

11. 31,680 ft = _?_ mi  **6**

12. 3 lb = _?_ oz  **48**

13. 15 qt = _?_ gal  **$3\frac{3}{4}$**

**Write which metric unit you would probably use to measure each item. Then write which customary unit you would probably use.**

14. water in a swimming pool  **kL; gal**

15. width of a door  **cm, m; in., ft**

16. weight of a 15-year old male  **kg; lb**

17. soup spoon  **mg; oz**

**18. Yes; the dimensions of the box are 40 mm by 25 mm.**

**19. 135 tons**

**Applications**

18. **Archaeology** The dimensions of an arrowhead are shown in the illustration at the right. Will this arrowhead fit in a box that is 0.04 m long and 2.5 cm wide? Explain your reasoning.

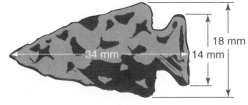

18 mm

34 mm

14 mm

19. **Biology** About 200 million years ago, the largest living animal was a dinosaur called a brachiosaurus. It weighed about 170,000 pounds. Today the largest living animal is the blue whale. It weighs about 220 tons. How many more tons does today's blue whale weigh than the brachiosaurus?

20. **Ecology** Every ton of recycled office paper saves about 17 trees. Glencoe/McGraw-Hill's office in Westerville, Ohio, recycled 32,634 pounds of paper in 1995. How many trees did this save?  **about 277 trees**

# Using Proportions

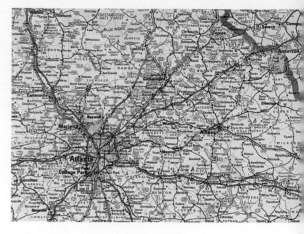

## What YOU'LL LEARN

• To use proportions to solve problems.

## Why IT'S IMPORTANT

You can use proportions to solve many real-life problems involving cooking, sports, and photography.

If you are planning a trip to a town you have never visited, you probably would look at a road map to see what roads to take. On the map, you might find a scale that says one inch equals approximately 18.2 miles or 29.2 kilometers.

The scale on a map is the ratio of the distance on the map to the actual distance. A **ratio** is a comparison of two numbers by division. The ratio that compares 5 to 146 can be written as follows.

$$5 \text{ to } 146 \qquad 5{:}146 \qquad 5 \text{ out of } 146 \qquad \frac{5}{146}$$

When you know the scale of a map, you can find the actual distances by writing and solving proportions. A **proportion** is an equation that shows that two ratios are equivalent. The **cross products** in the proportion below are $9 \cdot 24$ and $12 \cdot 18$. In a proportion, the two cross products are equal.

$$\frac{9}{12} = \frac{18}{24} \qquad \begin{array}{l} 12 \cdot 18 \\ 9 \cdot 24 \end{array} \qquad \begin{array}{l} 12 \cdot 18 = 216 \\ 9 \cdot 24 = 216 \end{array}$$

You can use the fact that cross products are equal to solve proportions.

**Example**  Solve each proportion.

**a.** $\dfrac{c}{36} = \dfrac{15}{24}$

$c \cdot 24 = 36 \cdot 15$    *Cross products are equal.*

$24c = 540$    *Multiply.*

$\dfrac{24c}{24} = \dfrac{540}{24}$    *Divide each side by 24.*

$c = 22.5$

The solution is 22.5.

**b.** $\dfrac{7}{12} = \dfrac{1.68}{d}$

$7 \cdot d = 12 \cdot 1.68$    *Cross products are equal.*

$d = \dfrac{12 \cdot 1.68}{7}$

$12 \;\boxed{\times}\; 1.68 \;\boxed{\div}\; 7 \;\boxed{=}\; \mathit{2.88}$

Thus, $d = 2.88$.

The solution is 2.88.

Proportions can be used to solve many real-life problems.

**Example**  The distance between Houston and San Antonio on a map is 6.2 inches. The scale on the map is 1 inch:30 miles. Find the distance between Houston and San Antonio.

$$\begin{array}{c} \textit{map distance} \\ \textit{actual distance} \end{array} \begin{array}{c} \rightarrow \\ \rightarrow \end{array} \frac{1 \text{ inch}}{30 \text{ miles}} = \frac{6.2 \text{ inches}}{n} \begin{array}{c} \leftarrow \\ \leftarrow \end{array} \begin{array}{c} \textit{map distance} \\ \textit{actual distance} \end{array}$$

$$1 \cdot n = 6.2 \cdot 30$$

$$n = 186$$

The actual distance between Houston and San Antonio is about 186 miles.

**Example** **3** A tree casts a shadow 19.5 meters long at the same time a 2-meter post casts a shadow 3 meters long. How tall is the tree?

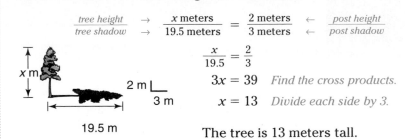

$$\underset{\text{tree shadow}}{\overset{\text{tree height}}{}} \rightarrow \frac{x \text{ meters}}{19.5 \text{ meters}} = \frac{2 \text{ meters}}{3 \text{ meters}} \leftarrow \underset{\text{post shadow}}{\overset{\text{post height}}{}}$$

$$\frac{x}{19.5} = \frac{2}{3}$$

$3x = 39$    *Find the cross products.*

$x = 13$    *Divide each side by 3.*

The tree is 13 meters tall.

# EXERCISES

**Practice**

**2. Answers will vary. The cross products are not equal.**

1. **Write** the cross products for $\frac{1}{2} = \frac{x}{8}$.   $1 \cdot 8 = 2 \cdot x$

2. **Write** two ratios that do not form a proportion. Explain why they do not.

**Solve each proportion.**

3. $\frac{m}{4} = \frac{7}{14}$   **2**
4. $\frac{a}{3} = \frac{10}{15}$   **2**
5. $\frac{28}{35} = \frac{8}{r}$   **10**
6. $\frac{14}{t} = \frac{4}{6}$   **21**

7. $\frac{8}{14} = \frac{12}{y}$   **21**
8. $\frac{10}{6} = \frac{h}{26}$   **$43\frac{1}{3}$**
9. $\frac{c}{2} = \frac{7}{4.2}$   **$3\frac{1}{3}$**
10. $\frac{0.7}{n} = \frac{2.1}{18}$   **6**

**Write a proportion that could be used to solve for each variable. Then solve the proportion.**   **14. 225**

11. $\frac{5}{c} = \frac{2}{8}$

12. $\frac{625}{5} = \frac{b}{2}$

13. $\frac{n}{5} = \frac{8}{2}$

14. $\frac{60}{4} = \frac{m}{15}$

15. $\frac{2}{0.98} = \frac{3}{d}$

16. $\frac{18}{3.375} = \frac{27}{z}$

11. 5 quarts fill $c$ cups
    2 quarts fill 8 cups   **20**

12. 625 bushels for 5 acres
    $b$ bushels for 2 acres   **250**

13. $n$ boxes in 5 crates
    8 boxes in 2 crates   **20**

14. 60 sliced mushrooms on 4 pizzas
    $m$ sliced mushrooms on 15 pizzas

15. 2 liters at $0.98
    3 liters at $$d$   **$1.47**

16. 18 plums weigh 3.375 pounds
    27 plums weigh $z$ pounds   **5.0625**

**Applications**

17. **Geometry**   In geometry, figures that have the same shape but differ in size are called **similar figures**. Also, if two triangles are similar, then their corresponding sides are proportional. In the figure at the right, $\triangle ABC$ is similar to $\triangle ADE$. Find the value of $x$.   **12 m**

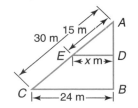

18. **$4\frac{1}{2}$ cups**

18. **Cooking**   Miguel is baking cookies for the class bake sale. The recipe calls for 3 cups of flour for 48 cookies. How many cups of flour are needed for 72 cookies?

19. **Sports**   Ken Griffey, Jr. got 3 hits in his first 8 at-bats. How many hits must he get in his next 200 at-bats to maintain this ratio?   **75 hits**

20. **Photography**   In simple cameras, like the one shown at the right, light from a subject passes through a lens and makes an image on film. The image and subject are always in proportion.

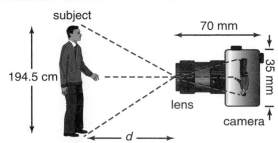

$$\frac{\text{image size}}{\text{subject size}} = \frac{\text{image distance from lens}}{\text{subject distance from lens}}$$

Find the distance represented by $d$ in the diagram.   **389 cm or 3.89 m**

# Geometry

A **point** is the simplest figure studied in geometry. A point is an exact location in space with no size or shape. A point can be represented by a dot and named with a capital letter.

Two points and all points on a straight path between them is called a **line segment**. A line segment is named by its endpoints. When two line segments have the same length, we say they are **congruent**.

If a segment connecting two points is extended indefinitely in both directions, it is called a **line**. Arrowheads are used to show that a line has no endpoints. A line can be named by two points on the line or with a single lowercase letter.

In geometry, a **ray** is defined as a segment that is extended indefinitely in one direction. A ray is named using the endpoint first and then any other point on the ray.

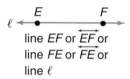

segment CD or $\overline{CD}$ or
segment DC or $\overline{DC}$

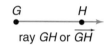

line EF or $\overleftrightarrow{EF}$ or
line FE or $\overleftrightarrow{FE}$ or
line $\ell$

ray GH or $\overrightarrow{GH}$

**Example** ❶ **Name two points, a line, two rays, and a line segment in the figure at the right.**

Two of the points are *A* and *B*.

You can use a single lowercase letter or any two points labeled on the line. So you can name it *n*, $\overleftrightarrow{AB}$, $\overleftrightarrow{AC}$, or $\overleftrightarrow{BC}$.

Two of the rays are $\overrightarrow{BC}$ and $\overrightarrow{BA}$.

One of the line segments shown is $\overline{AC}$.

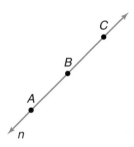

When two rays have a common endpoint, they form an **angle**. The common endpoint is called the **vertex**, and the rays are called the **sides**. An angle is named using three points with the vertex as the middle letter. If no other angle shares the same vertex, the angle can be named with just the vertex letter or with a numeral. Two angles that have the same measure are also said to be congruent.

*To say the measure of angle DEF is 120 degrees, we write m∠DEF = 120°.*

Another basic geometric figure is a **plane**. A plane is a flat surface with no edges, or boundaries. It can be named by a single uppercase script letter or by using any three points on the plane.

Two lines that lie in the same plane and never intersect are called **parallel lines**.

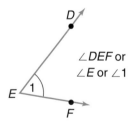

∠DEF or
∠E or ∠1

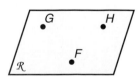

Plane FGH or plane $\mathcal{R}$

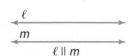

$\ell \parallel m$

A line that intersects two other lines is called a **transversal**.

| | |
|---|---|
| ***Congruent Angles with Parallel Lines*** | If a pair of parallel lines is intersected by a transversal, these pairs of angles are congruent.<br><br>**alternate interior angles:**<br>$\angle 3 \cong \angle 5, \angle 4 \cong \angle 6$<br>**alternate exterior angles:**<br>$\angle 1 \cong \angle 7, \angle 2 \cong \angle 8$<br>**corresponding angles:**<br>$\angle 1 \cong \angle 5, \angle 2 \cong \angle 6, \angle 3 \cong \angle 7, \angle 4 \cong \angle 8$ 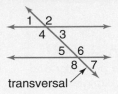 |

**Example** ❷ In the figure, $m \parallel n$ and $m\angle 1 = 110°$.

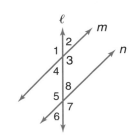

a. **Find $m\angle 7$.**

$\angle 1$ and $\angle 7$ are alternate exterior angles.

They are congruent so their measures are the same. $m\angle 7 = 110°$

b. **Find $m\angle 3$.**

$\angle 3$ and $\angle 7$ are corresponding angles.

Their measures are congruent, so $m\angle 3 = 110°$.

# EXERCISES

**Practice**

1–11. See Teacher's Answer Key.

**Draw and label a diagram to represent each of the following.**

1. point $A$
2. line $b$
3. plane $XYZ$
4. $\overline{EF}$
5. $\overrightarrow{GH}$
6. $\angle D$
7. $\overleftrightarrow{AB} \parallel \overline{CD}$
8. $\angle TUV$
9. $\overrightarrow{RS}$

**Draw $\overleftrightarrow{AB} \parallel \overleftrightarrow{CD}$ and transversal $\overleftrightarrow{EF}$.**

10. Name the interior angles.
    $\angle 3, \angle 4, \angle 5, \angle 6$

11. Name the exterior angles.
    $\angle 1, \angle 2, \angle 7, \angle 8$

**In the figure below, $\ell \parallel m$ and $m\angle 1 + m\angle 2 = 180°$. If $m\angle 1 = 49°$, find the measure of each angle.**

12. $\angle 2$  **131°**
13. $\angle 7$  **49°**
14. $\angle 8$  **131°**
15. $\angle 5$  **49°**
16. $\angle 3$  **49°**
17. $\angle 6$  **131°**

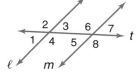

**Applications**

18. Sample answer: The ends of the three legs determine a plane.

19a. line segment

19b. 4 pairs

18. **Carpentry** Mrs. Kwan wants to build some stools that won't wobble. Explain why she should make the stools with three legs.

19. **Traffic** The shape of a stop sign is a regular octagon.
    a. What geometric figure does each edge of a stop sign represent?
    b. How many pairs of edges in a stop sign are parallel?

20. **Carpentry** A carpenter uses a protractor and a plumb line (a string with a weight attached) to measure the angle between a cathedral ceiling and the supporting wall. If $m\angle CXA = 115°$, find $m\angle CWB$.  **115°**

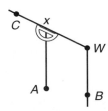

# Perimeter and Area

## What YOU'LL LEARN

- To find the perimeter and area of rectangles and squares, and
- to find the area of triangles, trapezoids, and circles.

## Why IT'S IMPORTANT

You can use perimeter and area to solve problems involving gardening and home maintenance.

The distance around a geometric figure is called its **perimeter**. Below are all the different rectangles that have a perimeter of 16 and sides with measures that are whole numbers. You can find the perimeter of each by counting.

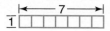 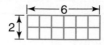  

Perimeter can also be found by doubling the sum of the length and the width.

$$P = 2(1 + 7) \qquad P = 2(2 + 6) \qquad P = 2(3 + 5) \qquad P = 2(4 + 4)$$
$$= 16 \qquad\qquad = 16 \qquad\qquad = 16 \qquad\qquad = 16$$

The measure of the surface enclosed by a geometric figure is called its **area**. You can find the area of a rectangle by counting the number of 1-by-1 unit squares or by multiplying the measures of the length and the width.

$$A = 1 \cdot 7 \text{ or } 7 \qquad A = 2 \cdot 6 \text{ or } 12 \qquad A = 3 \cdot 5 \text{ or } 15 \qquad A = 4 \cdot 4 \text{ or } 16$$

| Perimeter and Area of a Rectangle | The perimeter of a rectangle is twice the sum of its length $\ell$ and width $w$. <br><br> $$P = 2(\ell + w)$$ <br> The area of a rectangle is the product of its length $\ell$ and width $w$. <br><br> $$A = \ell w$$ |
|---|---|

A square is a special rectangle in which the lengths of all the sides are equal. For this reason, the formula for the perimeter of square is $P = 4s$ and the formula for the area of a square is $A = s^2$.

**Example** **1** Find the perimeter and area of rectangle *ABCD*.

$P = 2(\ell + w)$
$P = 2(6 + 4)$
$P = 2(10)$ or 20    The perimeter is 20 inches.

$A = \ell w$
$A = 6 \cdot 4$ or 24    The area is 24 square inches.

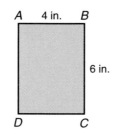

Use the formulas below to find the areas of other plane figures.

| Area Formulas for Parallelograms, Triangles, Trapezoids, and Circles | Parallelograms | Triangles | Trapezoids | Circles |
|---|---|---|---|---|
| | The area of a parallelogram is the base times the height. <br><br> $A = bh$ | The area of a triangle is one-half the base times the height. <br><br> $A = \frac{1}{2}bh$ | The area of a trapezoid is one-half the height times the sum of the bases. <br><br> $A = \frac{1}{2}h(b_1 + b_2)$ | The area of a circle is $\pi$ times the square of the radius. <br><br> $A = \pi r^2$ |

**Example** **2** **Find the area of each figure.**

**a.**

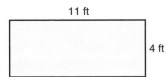
11 ft
4 ft

$A = bh$

$A = 11 \cdot 4$ or 44

The area is 44 ft$^2$.

**b.**

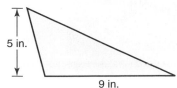
5 in.
9 in.

$A = \frac{1}{2}bh$

$A = \frac{1}{2}(5)(9)$ or $22\frac{1}{2}$

The area is $22\frac{1}{2}$ in$^2$.

**c.**

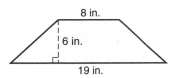
8 in.
6 in.
19 in.

$A = \frac{1}{2}h(b_1 + b_2)$

$A = \frac{1}{2} \cdot 6(8 + 19)$

$A = \frac{1}{2} \cdot \overset{3}{\underset{1}{\cancel{6}}} \cdot 27$ or 81

The area is 81 in$^2$.

**d.**

4 cm

$A = \pi r^2$

$A \approx 3.14(4^2)$

$A \approx 3.14(16)$

$A \approx 50.24$

The area is about 50 cm$^2$.

---

# EXERCISES

**Practice**

**1.** See students' work.

**2.** See students' work.

1. **Draw and label** a rectangle that has a perimeter of 12 inches.

2. **Draw and label** a triangle that has an area of 30 square centimeters.

**Find the perimeter and area of each figure.**

**3.**

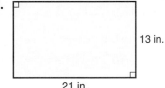
13 in.
21 in.

**68 in.; 273 in$^2$**

**4.**

4 cm

**16 cm; 16 cm$^2$**

**5.**

4 ft    5 ft
3 ft

**12 ft; 6 ft$^2$**

**Find the area of each figure.**

**6.**

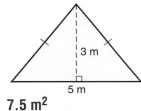
3 m
5 m

**7.5 m$^2$**

**7.**

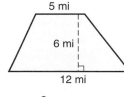
5 mi
6 mi
12 mi

**51 mi$^2$**

**8.**

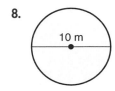
10 m

**78.5 m$^2$**

**Applications**

**9.** $278.64

9. **Home Maintenance**  How much will it cost to tile the floor of a rectangular room if the tiles cost $1.29/ft$^2$ and the room is 12 ft by 18 ft?

10. **Gardening**  Each participant in a community vegetable garden is allotted a rectangular-shaped plot that covers 1620 ft$^2$. Each plot is 18 ft wide.
   **a.** What is the length of each plot?   **90 ft**
   **b.** What is the perimeter of each plot?   **216 ft**

# Surface Area and Volume

**What YOU'LL LEARN**

- To find surface area and volume of prisms and cylinders.

**Why IT'S IMPORTANT**

You can use surface area and volume to solve problems involving pet care and manufacturing.

In geometry, we study three-dimensional figures. A three-dimensional figure that has two parallel congruent sides is called a prism. A **prism** is named by the shape of its parallel bases. The figure at the right is an example of a **rectangular prism**.

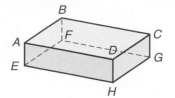

The amount of material that it would take to cover a three-dimensional figure is called the **surface area** of the figure. To find the surface area of a three-dimensional figure, find the area of each side of the figure. One way to find the surface area of a three-dimensional figure is to "unfold" it. The result is called a **net**. The surface area of a three-dimensional figure is the area of the net.

*A rectangular prism has six faces.*

**Example** ① **Find the surface area of a CD case that is 14.3 cm long, 12.4 cm wide, and 1.1 cm thick.**

Draw a net for the CD case and label the dimensions of each face. Use the formula $A = \ell w$ to find the areas of the faces.

Top and Bottom: 14.3 $\boxed{\times}$ 12.4 $\boxed{\times}$ 2 $\boxed{=}$ *354.64*

Two Sides: 12.4 $\boxed{\times}$ 1.1 $\boxed{\times}$ 2 $\boxed{=}$ *27.28*

Front and Back: 14.3 $\boxed{\times}$ 1.1 $\boxed{\times}$ 2 $\boxed{=}$ *31.46*

Add to find the total surface area.

Total: 354.64 $\boxed{+}$ 27.28 $\boxed{+}$ 31.46 $\boxed{=}$ *413.38*

The surface are of the CD case is 413.38 cm².

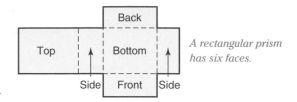

A can of soup is an example of a **cylinder**. The bases of a circular cylinder are two parallel, congruent circular regions. As with prisms, you find the surface area of a cylinder by finding the area of the two bases and adding the area of the curved side.

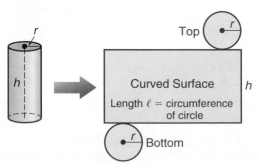

A net of a cylinder is shown at the left. Notice that the curved side is a rectangle that has the same height as the cylinder and the length is the same as the circumference of the base. Thus, the formula for the surface area of a circular prism is $2\pi r^2 + 2\pi rh$.

The amount a container will hold is called its capacity, or **volume**. Volume is usually measured in cubic units. To find the volume of a prism, multiply the area of the base times the height. You can use the formulas below to find the volumes of prisms and cylinders.

| | Prisms | Circular Cylinders |
|---|---|---|
| **Volume Formulas for Prisms and Circular Cylinders** | The volume of a rectangular prism is the area of the base times the height.<br><br>$V = Bh$ | The volume of a circular cylinder is the product of $\pi$, the square of the radius, and the height.<br><br>$V = \pi r^2 h$ |

**Example** ② **Find the volume of the cylinder. Use 3.14 for $\pi$.**

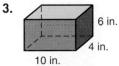

14 cm
20 cm

$V = \pi r^2 h$ *Formula for volume*

$V = 3.14 \cdot 7^2 \cdot 20$ *The diameter of the cylinder is 14 cm so*

$V \approx 3077$ *the radius is 7 cm.*

The volume is about 3077 cm³.

## EXERCISES

**Practice**

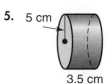

1.

3
8.5
Circum.
3

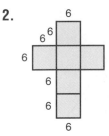

2.

6
6 6
6
6
6
6

3. 248 in²; 240 in³
4. 216 in²; 216 in³

1. **Draw and label** a net for a circular cylinder that has a diameter of 3 inches and a height of 8.5 inches.

2. **Draw and label** a net for a cube with sides that have a length of 6 inches.

**Find the surface area and volume of each three-dimensional figure. Use 3.14 for $\pi$. Round to the nearest tenth.**   5. 266.9 cm²; 274.8 cm³

3.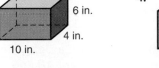
6 in.
4 in.
10 in.

4.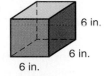
6 in.
6 in.
6 in.

5. 5 cm
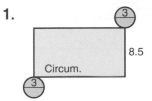
3.5 cm

6.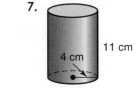
3 cm
7 cm    12 cm

282 cm²; 252 cm³

7.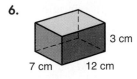
11 cm
4 cm

376.8 cm²; 552.6 cm³

8.
1 ft    10 ft

33.0 ft²; 7.85 ft³

**Applications**

9a. about 71,315.68 in²
or about 495.25 ft²

9b. about 1,088,952 in³
or about 630.18 ft³

9. **Manufacturing**  A cylindrical tank is being built for a tank truck. The tank is supposed to be 25 feet long and have a radius of 34 inches.
   a. How much material is needed to build the tank?
   b. What will be the volume of the tank when it is completed?

10. **Pet Care**  Jeremy has an end table that doubles as a fish tank. The base of the table is a rectangle that is 10 inches wide and 26 inches long. The table is 25 inches tall.
    a. What is the surface area of the table?   **2320 in²**
    b. How many cubic feet of water does it hold?   **about 3.76 ft³**

# The Pythagorean Theorem

**What YOU'LL LEARN**

- To use the Pythagorean theorem.

**Why IT'S IMPORTANT**

You can use the Pythagorean theorem to solve problems involving sports, safety, and surveying.

On grid paper, the length of each square is defined as one unit. Therefore, a square with sides 1 unit long has an area of 1 square unit.

The model at the right shows what the Greek mathematician Pythagoras learned about right triangles. A **right triangle** has one angle that measures 90°. This angle is called a **right angle**. The side opposite the right angle is called the **hypotenuse**. The sides that form the right angle are called the **legs**. Note that the sum of the squares of the lengths of the legs is equal to the square of the length of the hypotenuse.

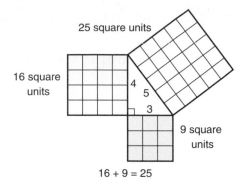

25 square units

16 square units

9 square units

16 + 9 = 25

Today we call this relationship the **Pythagorean theorem**. It is true for *any* right triangle.

| **Pythagorean Theorem** | **If *a* and *b* are the measures of the legs of a right triangle and *c* is the measure of the hypotenuse, then $c^2 = a^2 + b^2$.** |
|---|---|

**Example**  *ABCD* **is a rectangle. What is the length of** $\overline{AC}$**?**

Segments *AC*, *AB*, and *BC* form a right triangle. The legs of the right triangle are $\overline{AB}$ and $\overline{BC}$, and the hypotenuse of the right triangle is $\overline{AC}$.

$a^2 + b^2 = c^2$   *Pythagorean theorem*

$9^2 + 12^2 = c^2$   *Replace a with 9 and b with 12.*

$81 + 144 = c^2$

$225 = c^2$

$\sqrt{225} = c$   *Take the square root of each side.*

$15 = c$

The length of $\overline{AC}$ is 15 inches.

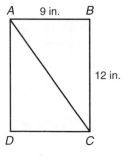

A   9 in.   B

12 in.

D   C

You can use the Pythagorean theorem to find the length of a leg of a right triangle if you know the length of the other leg and the hypotenuse.

**Example** **2**  Find the value of *b* in the triangle below.

$$a^2 + b^2 = c^2$$
$$15^2 + b^2 = 39^2$$
$$225 + b^2 = 1521$$
$$225 - 225 + b^2 = 1521 - 225$$
$$b^2 = 1296$$
$$b = \sqrt{1296}$$
$$b = 36$$

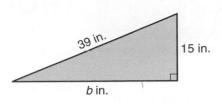

The value of *b* is 36.

# EXERCISES

**Practice**

1. **Write** an equation that describes the relationship among the three large squares in the figure at the right. **$6^2 + 8^2 = 10^2$**

2. **Draw and label** a right triangle with a hypotenuse of 20 units and legs of 12 units and 16 units.

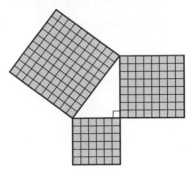

2.

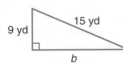

**Find the missing lengths. Round decimal answers to the nearest tenth.**

3.

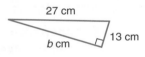

**12 yd**

4.

**23.7 cm**

5. 13 in. *a* in. 18 in.

**12.4 in.**

**In a right triangle, if *a* and *b* are the measures of the legs and *c* is the measure of the hypotenuse, find each missing measure. Round decimal answers to the nearest tenth.**

6. $a = 6, b = 5$  **7.8**    7. $a = 12, b = 12$  **17.0**    8. $a = 8, b = 16$  **17.9**

9. $a = 20, c = 25$  **15**    10. $a = 9, c = 14$  **10.7**    11. $b = 15, c = 20$  **13.2**

12. $a = 5, b = 50$  **50.2**    13. $b = 54, c = 68$  **41.3**    14. $a = 4.5, c = 8.5$  **7.2**

**Applications**

15. **Sports**  In football, receivers often run a pass route called the "down and out." The route runs down the field, parallel to the sideline, then turns 90° toward the sideline. How far from his original position is a receiver who runs downfield 12 yards, turns and runs toward the sideline for another 5 yards?  **13 yards**

16. **Safety**  The National Safety Council recommends placing the base of a ladder one foot from the wall for every three feet of the ladder's length.
    a. How far away from a wall should you place a 30-foot ladder?  **10 feet**
    b. How high can the ladder reach safely?  **about 28.3 feet**

17. **Surveying**  To determine the distance across a pond, surveyors made the diagram at the right. Write an equation they can use to determine how far it is across the lake. Then solve.
    **$450^2 = 200^2 + b^2$; about 403.1 ft**

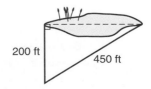

# Counting Outcomes and Probability

### *What* YOU'LL LEARN

- To count outcomes using a tree diagram or the fundamental counting principle, and
- to find the probability of a simple event.

### *Why* IT'S IMPORTANT

You can use probability to calculate the chance that something will happen. This is especially helpful in games.

Suppose you decide to guess on the answers to a quiz with four true-false questions on it. How many different sets of answers, or **outcomes**, are possible? You can draw a diagram to find all the possible outcomes.

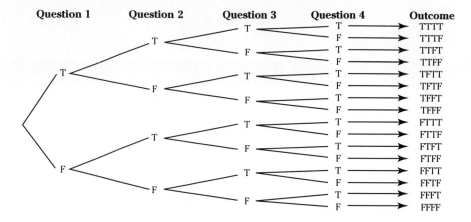

There are 16 different sets of guesses, or outcomes.

The diagram above is called a **tree diagram**. You can also find the total number of outcomes by multiplying. This principle is known as the **fundamental counting principle**.

| **Fundamental Counting Principle** | **If event *M* can occur in *m* ways and is followed by event *N* that can occur in *n* ways, then the event *M* followed by the event *N* can occur in *m · n* ways.** |
|---|---|

The number of possible outcomes for the quiz can be determined by using this principle. Each question has two outcomes and there are four questions. So, the number of outcomes is $2 \cdot 2 \cdot 2 \cdot 2$ or 16.

**Example**  **A number cube is rolled once, and a coin is tossed once. How many outcomes are possible?**

| *number of outcomes for number cube* | × | *number of outcomes for coin* | = | *number of possible outcomes* |
|---|---|---|---|---|
| 6 | × | 2 | = | 12 |

There are 12 possible outcomes.

When all outcomes have an *equally likely* chance of happening, we say that the outcomes happen at **random**.

**Probability** is the chance that an event will happen. The probability of an outcome is written as a number from 0 to 1.

| *Definition of Probability* | $$\text{Probability} = \frac{\text{number of ways an event can occur}}{\text{number of possible outcomes}}$$ |
|---|---|

**Example** **2** A spinner like the one at the right is used in a game. What is the probability that the spinner will stop on blue when you spin it?

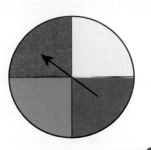

There is one way to stop on blue.

There are 4 possible outcomes.

$$P(\text{blue}) = \frac{\text{number of ways to stop on blue}}{\text{number of possible outcomes}} = \frac{1}{4}$$

## EXERCISES

**Practice**

**1.**

red
yellow
green
blue

**2.** See student's work; possible answer: What is the probability of a red coin landing on heads?

**3.** No section on the spinner is white.

**4.**

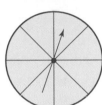

1. **Draw** a tree diagram to list all the outcomes for Example 2.

2. **Write** a problem that corresponds to the tree diagram at the right.

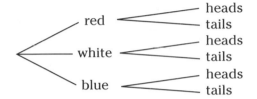

red — heads / tails
white — heads / tails
blue — heads / tails

3. **Explain** why the probability of stopping on white on the spinner in Example 2 is 0.

4. **Draw** a spinner where the probability of an outcome is $\frac{1}{8}$.

**Find the number of possible outcomes for each event.**

5. two number cubes are rolled   **36**   6. a coin is tossed three times   **6**

7. a spinner with 5 equal sections is spun twice   **25**

**A drawer contains one red sock, three blue socks, two black socks, and two green socks. One sock is removed. Find each probability.**

8. $P(\text{red})$ $\frac{1}{8}$   9. $P(\text{blue})$ $\frac{3}{8}$   10. $P(\text{not black})$ $\frac{3}{4}$

11. $P(\text{green})$ $\frac{1}{4}$   12. $P(\text{orange})$ **0**   13. $P(\text{red or blue})$ $\frac{1}{2}$

**The spinner at the right is spun once. Find each probability.**

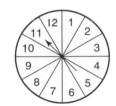

14. $P(\text{even})$ $\frac{1}{2}$   15. $P(\text{odd})$ $\frac{1}{2}$

16. $P(\text{less than one})$ **0**   17. $P(\text{prime})$ $\frac{5}{12}$

**Applications**

18. **Fashion**   Paul has 7 shirts and 3 pairs of slacks. How many different outfits can he make using 1 shirt and 1 pair of slacks?   **21 outfits**

19. **Weather**   The TV weather reporter said that the probability of rain on Friday is 40%. What is the probability that it will not rain?   **60%**

20. **Retail Sales**   Mercedes surveyed 75 students to determine how many of each size of school jackets to order. The results of the survey are shown in the table at the right.

20a. $\frac{1}{5}$

20b. $\frac{8}{15}$

   **a.** If one of the students is chosen at random, what is the probability that the student wears a medium?

   **b.** If one of the students is chosen at random, what is the probability that the student wears a large or extra large?

| Size | Tally |
|---|---|
| Small | ⅏ ⅏ ⅏ ⅏ |
| Medium | ⅏ ⅏ ⅏ |
| Large | ⅏ ⅏ ⅏ ⅏ III |
| Extra Large | ⅏ ⅏ ⅏ II |

1. In a survey, parents were asked where their children prefer to do homework. The graph shows the results of the survey. If 1600 parents were surveyed, how many of them said their children preferred the kitchen? **C**

**Where Do Your Kids Do Their Homework?**

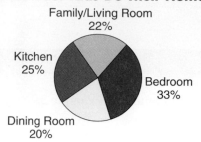

- Family/Living Room 22%
- Kitchen 25%
- Bedroom 33%
- Dining Room 20%

A  25
B  40
C  400
D  40,000
E  Not Here

2. The graph below shows a store's monthly sales of video games. **J**

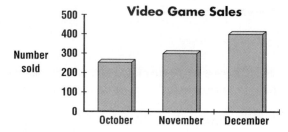

**Video Game Sales**

Number sold (0, 100, 200, 300, 400, 500)
October, November, December

The average price of a video game was $40. What would be a reasonable sales total, without tax, for the video games sold during the 3-month period?

F  Less than $28,000
G  Between $28,000 and $32,000
H  Between $32,000 and $36,000
J  Between $36,000 and $40,000
K  More than $40,000

3. The graph below shows school enrollment in the U.S. from 1966 to 1996.

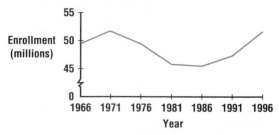

Enrollment (millions) (0, 45, 50, 55)
1966 1971 1976 1981 1986 1991 1996
Year

*(Continued at top of next column)*

Which is a reasonable conclusion from the information on the graph? **E**

A  A record high will be reached in 2001.
B  Enrollment was at a record low in 1981.
C  Enrollment reached its peak in 1971.
D  Enrollment decreased between 1966 and 1976.
E  Enrollment increased between 1986 and 1996.

4. A recipe that makes 12 servings calls for $4\frac{2}{3}$ cups of flour. How much flour is needed to make 24 servings? **H**

F  $2\frac{1}{3}$ c
G  $8\frac{2}{3}$ c
H  $9\frac{1}{3}$ c
J  $16\frac{2}{3}$ c
K  Not Here

5. In the United States flag, the length is $1\frac{9}{10}$ times the width. What is the length of a flag if its width is $4\frac{1}{2}$ feet? **D**

A  $2\frac{3}{5}$ ft
B  $4\frac{9}{20}$ ft
C  $6\frac{2}{5}$ ft
D  $8\frac{11}{20}$ ft
E  Not Here

6. Brian and three friends bought $\frac{3}{4}$ pound of trail mix. If they spilt the mix equally, how much will each person get? **G**

F  $\frac{1}{16}$ lb
G  $\frac{3}{16}$ lb
H  $\frac{3}{8}$ lb
J  $\frac{1}{4}$ lb
K  Not Here

7. How many slices of pepperoni, each $\frac{1}{16}$-inch thick, can be cut from a stick of pepperoni $4\frac{1}{2}$ inches long?  **A**

   **A** 72

   **B** 80

   **C** 128

   **D** 144

   **E** Not Here

8. After galloping $1\frac{7}{8}$ miles, a racehorse trotted an additional $\frac{7}{8}$ miles to cool down. How far did the horse travel altogether?  **J**

   **F** $1\frac{3}{4}$ mi

   **G** $2\frac{1}{8}$ mi

   **H** $2\frac{1}{4}$ mi

   **J** $2\frac{3}{4}$ mi

   **K** Not Here

9. A recipe calls for $2\frac{1}{3}$ cups of biscuit mix, $\frac{1}{2}$ cup of milk, $\frac{1}{4}$ cup of sugar, and $\frac{1}{4}$ cup of margarine. How many cups of ingredients are in the recipe?  **B**

   **A** $3\frac{1}{4}$ c

   **B** $3\frac{1}{3}$ c

   **C** $3\frac{5}{12}$ c

   **D** $3\frac{1}{2}$ c

   **E** Not Here

10. The tank of Zina's car holds 12 gallons of gas. It took $6\frac{1}{2}$ gallons to fill the tank. How much gasoline was already in the tank?  **G**

    **F** $4\frac{1}{2}$ gal

    **G** $5\frac{1}{2}$ gal

    **H** $6\frac{1}{2}$ gal

    **J** $18\frac{1}{2}$ gal

    **K** Not Here

11. Margurite weighed $7\frac{1}{2}$ pounds at birth. Her brother weighed $7\frac{3}{4}$ pounds when he was born. What was the difference in their birth weights?  **B**

    **A** $\frac{1}{8}$ lb

    **B** $\frac{1}{4}$ lb

    **C** $\frac{3}{8}$ lb

    **D** $\frac{1}{2}$ lb

    **E** Not Here

12. What is the approximate length of a large paper clip?  **G**

    **F** 4.8 millimeters

    **G** 48 millimeters

    **H** 48 centimeters

    **J** 4.8 meters

    **K** 0.048 kilometers

13. Roberta is driving a truck that weighs 55,600 pounds when fully loaded. A highway sign states that the maximum weight allowed is 28 tons. If Roberta's truck is fully loaded, how far is it away from the maximum?  **A**

    **A** 400 pounds

    **B** 6000 pounds

    **C** 3 tons

    **D** 400 tons

    **E** Not Here

14. According to the scale on a map, 1 inch represents 19.9 kilometers. If two cities are 180 kilometers apart, which proportion could be used to find $x$, the distance between the two cities on the map?  **F**

    **F** $\frac{1}{19.9} = \frac{x}{180}$

    **G** $\frac{180}{1} = \frac{x}{19.9}$

    **H** $\frac{19.9}{1} = \frac{x}{180}$

    **J** $\frac{x}{19.9} = \frac{1}{180}$

    **K** $\frac{1}{x} = \frac{180}{19.9}$

15. The ratio of your weight on the moon to your weight on Earth is 1:6. If your weight on Earth is 144 pounds, how much would you weigh on the moon?　**C**

   A  864 lb

   B  72 lb

   C  24 lb

   D  12 lb

   E  Not Here

16. Which figure best represents ray *XY*?　**G**

   F

   G

   H

   J

17. The sides of the trapezoid are best described as:　**E**

   A  rays

   B  points

   C  angles

   D  lines

   E  Not Here

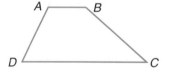

18. The length of 1 side of an equilateral triangle is 2.2 meters. What is its perimeter in *centimeters*?　**H**

   F  6.6 cm

   G  66 cm

   H  660 cm

   J  6600 cm

19. What is the area of the trapezoid?　**B**

   A  10 sq ft

   B  30 sq ft

   C  40 sq ft

   D  95 sq ft

20. What is the surface area of the cylinder? (Use $\pi \approx 3.14$.)　**J**

   F  401.92 sq cm

   G  427.04 sq cm

   H  452.16 sq cm

   J  854.08 sq cm

21. What is the volume of the cube?　**D**

   A  200 ft$^3$

   B  175 ft$^3$

   C  36 ft$^3$

   D  216 ft$^3$

   E  Not Here

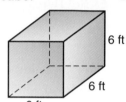

22. An airplane flies 3 miles due south, then 4 miles due west. How far is the airplane from its starting point?　**F**

   F  5 mi          J  25 mi

   G  6 mi          K  Not Here

   H  7 mi

23. A 15-foot ladder is leaning against a house. The base of the ladder is 5 feet from the house. How high does the ladder reach?　**B**

   A  40 ft          D  10 ft

   B  14.1 ft        E  Not Here

   C  15.8 ft

24. A number cube is tossed three times. How many outcomes are possible?　**J**

   F  18            J  216

   G  36            K  Not Here

   H  108

25. A bag contains 5 blue, 10 black, 5 red, and 5 yellow marbles. If you select one marble at random, what is the probability of selecting a black marble?　**A**

   A  $\frac{2}{5}$

   B  $\frac{1}{5}$

   C  $\frac{2}{9}$

   D  $\frac{1}{6}$

   E  Not Here

# CHAPTER A TEACHER'S ANSWER KEY

**Page A7   Prerequisite Concept 1**

9.

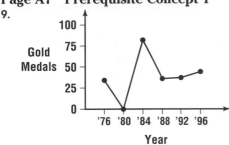

10.

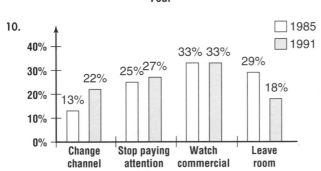

**Page A21   Prerequisite Concept 8**

1. • A

2.  b

3.

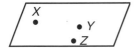

4. E●━━━━━━●F

5.

6.

7. A●   ●C
   │    │
   │    │
   B●   ●D

8.

9.
   R      S

10–11.

# To The Student

Chapter B contains four sections: pretest, review lessons, chapter tests, and posttest. The pretest is a review of the concepts that you will need to succeed in the second half of Algebra 1. You should take the pretest to determine which concepts you need to review. The review lessons allow you to develop, and eventually master, the individual skills the pretest

identified as needing to be reinforced. You should take the posttest to make sure you understand all of the concepts and to measure your progress.

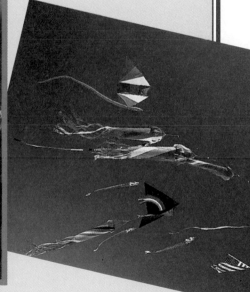

1. Write the expression $5 \cdot 5 \cdot m \cdot m \cdot m \cdot n \cdot n$ using exponents.  **C**

   A. $5m^3n^2$

   B. $5^2m^2n^2$

   C. $5^2m^3n^2$

   D. $5mn$

2. Name the property illustrated by $2(y + 5) = 2y + 10$.  **B**

   A. multiplicative identity property

   B. distributive property

   C. substitution property

   D. associative property of addition

3. Evaluate $3st^2 + 2s$ if $s = 5$ and $t = 3$.  **A**

   A. 145

   B. 55

   C. 100

   D. 141

4. Simplify $\frac{4^2 \div 2^3 + 11 \cdot 3}{10 - 3}$.  **C**

   A. 6

   B. $\frac{16}{287}$

   C. 5

   D. $\frac{39}{7}$

5. Simplify $-2x^2 + 3x + 5 + 4x^2 - 7x - 2$.  **D**

   A. $6x^2 - 4x + 3$

   B. $2x^2 - 10x + 3$

   C. $2x^2 + 4x - 3$

   D. $2x^2 - 4x + 3$

6. Simplify $\frac{5}{16} - \frac{2}{3}$.  **A**

   A. $-\frac{17}{48}$

   B. $\frac{17}{48}$

   C. $-\frac{3}{13}$

   D. $\frac{7}{24}$

7. Simplify $\frac{24x - 15y}{-3}$.  **B**

   A. $8x - 5y$

   B. $-8x + 5y$

   C. $-3xy$

   D. $-72x + 45y$

8. Evaluate $\sqrt{x^2 + y^2}$ for $x = 4$ and $y = 10$. Round to the nearest tenth if the result is not a whole number.  **B**

   A. 116

   B. 10.8

   C. 3.7

   D. 40

9. What is the solution of $45 = 39 - w$?  **C**

   A. 84

   B. 6

   C. $-6$

   D. 45

10. What is the solution of $\frac{1}{5}t = 35$?  **C**

    A. 7

    B. $\frac{1}{7}$

    C. 175

    D. 40

11. What is the solution of $5(x + 2) - 3 = 3x - 7$?  **A**

    A. $-7$

    B. $-3$

    C. 0

    D. $-\frac{7}{4}$

12. Solve $Q = \frac{13r}{5}$ for $r$.  **A**

    A. $r = \frac{5Q}{13}$

    B. $r = \frac{13Q}{5}$

    C. $r = \frac{Q - 5}{13}$

    D. $r = 65Q$

**13.** What is the solution of $\frac{5}{d} = \frac{25}{60}$?  **C**

   **A.** 60

   **B.** 5

   **C.** 12

   **D.** 275

**14.** What number is 16% of 160?  **B**

   **A.** 10

   **B.** 25.6

   **C.** 1000

   **D.** 185.6

**15.** A house built in 1982 originally cost $80,000. In 1994, the same house sold for $144,800. What was the percent of increase over the original price?  **C**

   **A.** 45%

   **B.** 80%

   **C.** 81%

   **D.** 90%

**16.** Jacqui Walker invested a portion of $20,000 at 5% simple interest and the balance at 8% simple interest. How much did she invest at each rate if her total annual income from both investments was $1510?  **B**

   **A.** $5000 at 5% and $15,000 at 8%

   **B.** $3000 at 5% and $17,000 at 8%

   **C.** $8500 at 5% and $13,562.50 at 8%

   **D.** $692.31 at 5% and $19,307.69 at 8%

**Use the graph at the right to answer Questions 17–19.**

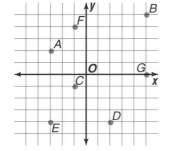

**17.** What is the ordered pair for point $D$?

   **A.** $(2, -4)$

   **B.** $(2, 4)$

   **C.** $(-4, 2)$

   **D.** $(4, -2)$  **A**

**18.** Name the quadrant in which point $A$ is located.  **B**

   **A.** I       **C.** III

   **B.** II      **D.** IV

**19.** What is the range of the relation graphed?  **B**

   **A.** $\{-3, -1, 2, 5\}$

   **B.** $\{-4, -1, 0, 2, 4, 5\}$

   **C.** {all the integers}

   **D.** $\{-4, -1, 2, 4, 5\}$

**20.** What is the $y$-intercept of the graph of $2x + 3y = 15$?  **B**

   **A.** 3       **C.** 2

   **B.** 5       **D.** 15

**21.** Which equation has a graph that is a vertical line?  **A**

   **A.** $x = 9$

   **B.** $x + y = 0$

   **C.** $y = -3$

   **D.** $x - y = 0$

**22.** Find the slope of the line that passes through $(3, 7)$ and $(11, 19)$.  **A**

   **A.** $\frac{3}{2}$       **C.** $\frac{2}{3}$

   **B.** $-\frac{3}{2}$     **D.** $\frac{13}{7}$

**23.** Find an equation of the line through $(0, 7)$ with slope 3.  **A**

   **A.** $-3x + y = 7$

   **B.** $3x + y = 7$

   **C.** $-x + 3y = 7$

   **D.** $x + 3y = -7$

**24.** A line that is parallel to the graph of $2x - 9y = 4$ has which of the following slopes?  **B**

   **A.** 2       **C.** $-\frac{9}{2}$

   **B.** $\frac{2}{9}$      **D.** $-\frac{2}{9}$

**25.** What are the coordinates of the midpoint of the segment whose endpoints are $(7, 1)$ and $(24, 13)$?  **B**

   **A.** $(8.5, 6)$      **C.** $(7, 15.5)$

   **B.** $(15.5, 7)$    **D.** $(10, 12.5)$

# Variables and Expressions

Any letter used to represent an unspecified number is called a **variable**. You can use variables to translate verbal expressions into algebraic expressions.

| Words | Symbols |
|---|---|
| 4 more than a number | $y + 4$ |
| a number decreased by 12 | $b - 12$ |
| the product of 3 and a number | $3t$ |
| a number divided by 8 | $h \div 8$ or $\frac{h}{8}$ |

The algebraic expression $x^n$ represents a product in which each factor is the same. The small raised $n$ is the exponent and it tells how many times the base, $x$, is used as a factor.

**Example**  Evaluate $2^5$.

$2^5 = 2 \cdot 2 \cdot 2 \cdot 2 \cdot 2$ or $32$

## EXERCISES

1–3. Sample answers are given.

1. one more than $z$

2. two fifths times the square of $b$

3. fifty-seven decreased by three times $q$

8. $n + 17$

9. $7n - 25$

**Write a verbal expression for each algebraic expression.**

1. $z + 1$
2. $\frac{2}{5}b^2$
3. $57 - 3q$

**Write an algebraic expression for each verbal expression.**

4. a number increased by 14   $n + 14$
5. six times a number   $6n$
6. 12 more than a number   $12 + n$
7. a number divided by 4   $n \div 4$
8. the sum of a number and 17
9. 25 less than 7 times a number
10. three times the sum of a number and 13   $3(n + 13)$
11. 74 decreased by twice the cube of a number   $74 - 2n^3$

**Write each expression as an expression with exponents.**

12. $9 \cdot 9 \cdot 9 \cdot 9$   $9^4$
13. $27 \cdot a \cdot a \cdot a$   $27a^3$
14. $14(w)(w)$   $14w^2$

**Evaluate each expression.**

15. $3^3$   27
16. $5^2$   25
17. $10^4$   10,000

18. **Environment** According to the American Water Works Association, it takes an average of 20 gallons of water to wash dishes by hand and as much as 25 gallons of water to run a dishwasher.
    a. Write an expression representing the amount of water used to wash dishes by hand for $x$ washes.   $20x$
    b. Write an expression representing the amount of water needed to run a dishwasher for $x$ washes.   $25x$
    c. Write an expression representing the difference between the amount of water needed to run a dishwasher and the amount of water used to wash dishes by hand for $x$ washes.   $25x - 20x$

# Patterns and Sequences

When solving certain problems, you must often look for a pattern. A **pattern** is a repeated design or arrangement.

**Example ❶** Study the pattern at the right. Draw the next three figures in the pattern.

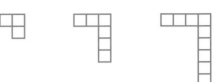

The pattern begins by adding one square to the left end of the horizontal piece and two squares to the bottom of the vertical piece, then continues in the same pattern. The next three figures are drawn below.

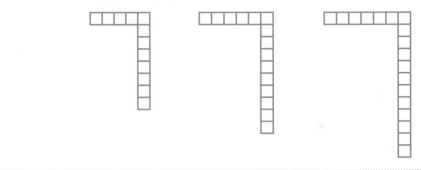

The numbers 1, 3, 5, 7, 9, and 11 form a **sequence**. A sequence is a set of numbers in a specific order. The numbers in a sequence are called **terms**.

**Example ❷** Find the next three numbers in each sequence.

a. 5, 10, 20, 40, . . .  Study the pattern in the sequence. Each term is twice the term before it. The next three terms are 80, 160, and 320.

b. 729, 243, 81, . . .  Study the pattern in the sequence. Each term is $\frac{1}{3}$ of the term before it. The next three terms are 27, 9, and 3.

## EXERCISES

**Give the next two items for each pattern.**

1.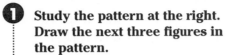

2. ⊗ ; The pattern repeats in sets of 3 and the 22nd figure is the first member of the 8th set.

2. What does the 22nd figure in Exercise 1 look like? Explain your reasoning.

3. $w - 45, w - 40, w - 35, w - 30, . . .$  **$w - 25, w - 20$**

4. 5, 7, 5, 9, 5, 11, 5, 13, 5, . . .  **15, 5**

5. **Transportation**  Keisha knows that trains arrive regularly at the train station. She has part of the afternoon schedule. When will the next train arrive at the station?  **4:46 P.M.**

| Train Schedule |
| --- |
| Arrivals: |
| 3:40 P.M. |
| 4:02 P.M. |
| 4:24 P.M. |

# Order of Operations

Ian said Shelley won first prize and I won second prize. Without punctuation, this sentence has three possible meanings.

Ian said, "Shelley won first prize and I won second prize."

"Ian," said Shelley, "won first prize and I won second prize."

Ian said Shelley won first prize and I [that is, the speaker] won second prize.

In mathematics, in order to avoid confusion about meaning, an agreed-upon order of operations tells us whether a mathematical expression such as $45 - 15 \div 5$ means $(45 - 15) \div 5$ or $45 - (15 \div 5)$. That order is shown below.

| Order of Operations |
| --- |
| 1. Simplify expressions inside grouping symbols. |
| 2. Evaluate all powers. |
| 3. Do all multiplications and divisions from left to right. |
| 4. Do all additions and subtractions from left to right. |

You can evaluate an algebraic expression when the value of each variable is known. Replace each variable with its value and then use the order of operations to perform the indicated operations. Remember to do all operations within grouping symbols first.

**Example**

a. Simplify $45 - 15 \div 5$.

$$45 - 15 \div 5 = 45 - 3$$
$$= 42$$

b. Evaluate $a^2 - 8(b + 7)$ if $a = 10$ and $b = 2$.

$$a^2 - 8(b + 7) = 10^2 - 8(2 + 7)$$
$$= 10^2 - 8(9)$$
$$= 100 - 8(9)$$
$$= 100 - 72 \text{ or } 28$$

## EXERCISES

**Evaluate each expression.**

1. $18 - 2 \cdot 3$  **12**

2. $4^2 \div 8 - 3^3 \cdot \frac{1}{3} + 4 \cdot 6$  **17**

3. $5(36 - 31) + 2 \cdot 7$  **39**

4. $\frac{70 - 25}{7 + 8}$  **3**

**Evaluate each expression when $a = 4$, $b = 2$, $x = \frac{1}{2}$, and $y = \frac{1}{3}$.**

5. $8a - 2b$  **28**

6. $10x + 9y$  **8**

7. $48x^2 - (3a - 5b)$  **10**

8. $\frac{a^2 + b^2}{5y^2}$  **36**

9. **Accounting**  Della and James are selling tickets for a dinner theater performance. Combination tickets for dinner and the performance cost $15. Performance only tickets cost $9.

   a. If Della and James sell both types of tickets, write an expression for the total amount of money they collect.  **$15(d + j) + 9(d + j)$**

   b. Della sells 20 combination tickets and 15 performance tickets. James sells 18 combination tickets and 24 performance tickets. How much money have they collected?  **$921**

# Integration: Statistics
# Stem-and-Leaf Plots

Mrs. Cortez interviewed some students who were willing to help her with some typing. The number of words typed per minute by each student is listed below.

16    21    18    17    18    20    15    16

This data can be organized on a **stem-and-leaf plot**. The greatest common place value of each piece of data is used to form the **stem**. The next greatest place value is used to form the **leaves**.

| Stem | Leaf |
|---|---|
| 1 | 8 8 7 6 6 5 |
| 2 | 1 0 |

*1 | 7 = 17 words per minute*

Data with more than two digits may be rounded $13.5 \Rightarrow 14$ or truncated $13.\cancel{5} \Rightarrow 13$ . The rounded or truncated values of the data at the right can be compared in a back-to-back stem-and-leaf plot.

| 21.7 | 37.3 | 25.5 |
|---|---|---|
| 33.4 | 31.9 | 24.3 |
| 42.6 | 43.8 | 32.7 |
| 28.2 | 29.1 | 24.5 |

| Rounded | Stem | Truncated |
|---|---|---|
| 9 8 6 5 4 2 | 2 | 1 4 4 5 8 9 |
| 7 3 3 2 | 3 | 1 2 3 7 |
| 4 3 | 4 | 2 3 |

In a back-to-back stem-and-leaf plot, the same stem is used for the leaves of both plots.

---

## EXERCISES

**Solve each problem.**

1. The stem-and-leaf plot at the right shows the height, in feet, of buildings in Boston that are at least 500 feet tall.

   | Stem | Leaf |
   |---|---|
   | 5 | 5 3 2 1 0 0 |
   | 6 | 1 0 0 0 0 |
   | 7 | 5 |
   | 8 | 0 |

   *5 | 2 = 520 feet*

   a. How tall is the tallest building? **800 feet**

   b. What is the height of the shortest building represented in the plot? **500 feet**

   c. What building height occurs most frequently? **600 feet**

2. Danielle is a sales clerk at a bagel shop. Her sales for the first week were $58, $64, $26, $79, and $55. Her sales for the second week were $39, $72, $64, $52, and $78. **a. See Teacher's Answer Key.**

   a. Make a stem-and-leaf plot of Danielle's two weeks' sales.

   b. What is the greatest value of sales that Danielle made in one day during the two-week period? **$79**

# Open Sentences

Mathematical statements with one or more variables are called **open sentences**. Open sentences are **solved** by finding a replacement for the variable that results in a true sentence. The replacement is called a **solution**.

**Example** ➊ Replace $y$ in $5y - 9 = 21$ with the value 6.

$5y - 9 = 21$

$5(6) - 9 = 21$

$30 - 9 = 21$

$21 = 21$   true

Since $y = 6$ makes the sentence $5y - 9 = 21$ true, 6 is a solution.

A set of numbers from which replacements for a variable may be chosen is called a **replacement set**. The set of all replacements for the variable in an open sentence that results in a true sentence is called the **solution set** for the sentence.

A sentence that contains an equals sign, =, is called an **equation** and sometimes may be solved by simply applying the order of operations. A sentence having the symbols < or > is called an **inequality**.

**Example** ➋ Solve $\frac{3(4 + 5)}{2 \cdot 4 - 3} = w$.

$\frac{3(4 + 5)}{2 \cdot 4 - 3} = w$

$\frac{3(9)}{8 - 3} = w$

$\frac{27}{5} = w$

## EXERCISES

**State whether each equation is true or false for the value of the variable given.**

1. $2q - 6 = 13$, $q = 10$   **false**
2. $3s^2 < 30$, $s = 4$   **false**
3. $5t + 2t^2 = 33$, $t = 3$   **true**
4. $\frac{4x + 5}{x^2} = 9$, $x = 1$   **true**

**Solve each equation.**

5. $d = 2(4 \cdot 5 - 3^2)$   **22**
6. $m = 5\frac{2}{5} - 1\frac{3}{10}$   **$4\frac{1}{10}$**
7. $\frac{40 - 15}{5 + 6} = z$   **$2\frac{3}{11}$**

8. **Business**   Saundra must sell 4 t-shirts to make $10 profit.

8a. $t = 60\left(\frac{4}{10}\right)$

   a. Write an equation that represents the number of t-shirts she must sell to make $60 profit.

   b. How many t-shirts would she have to sell?   **24**

# Identity and Equality Properties

The identity and equality properties in the chart below can help you solve algebraic equations and evaluate mathematical expressions.

| Additive Identity Property | For any number $a$, $a + 0 = 0 + a = a$. |
|---|---|
| Multiplicative Identity Property | For any number $a$, $a \cdot 1 = 1 \cdot a = a$. |
| Multiplicative Property of Zero | For any number $a$, $a \cdot 0 = 0 \cdot a = 0$. |
| Substitution Property of Equality | For any numbers $a$ and $b$, if $a = b$ then $a$ may be replaced by $b$ in any expression. |
| Reflexive Property of Equality | For any number $a$, $a = a$. |
| Symmetric Property of Equality | For any numbers $a$ and $b$, if $a = b$, then $b = a$. |
| Transitive Property of Equality | For any numbers $a$, $b$, and $c$, if $a = b$ and $b = c$, then $a = c$. |

**Example**

Evaluate $36 \cdot 1 + 9 + 12(2 \cdot 3 - 6)$. Indicate the property used in each step.

$$
\begin{aligned}
36 \cdot 1 + 9 + 12(2 \cdot 3 - 6) &= 36 \cdot 1 + 9 + 12(6 - 6) && \textit{Substitution } (=) \\
&= 36 \cdot 1 + 9 + 12(0) && \textit{Substitution } (=) \\
&= 36 + 9 + 12(0) && \textit{Identity } (\times) \\
&= 36 + 9 + 0 && \textit{Mult. prop. of 0} \\
&= 45 + 0 && \textit{Substitution } (=) \\
&= 45 && \textit{Identity } (+)
\end{aligned}
$$

## EXERCISES

**Solve each equation.**

**1.** $w(34) = 0$   **0**    **2.** $7 \cdot x = 7$   **1**    **3.** $0 + r = 15$   **15**   **4.** $9(0) = a$   **0**

**Name the property or properties illustrated by each statement.**

**5.** $(0)3 = 0$   **Mult. Prop. of zero**     **6.** $10 \cdot 1 = 10$   **Mult. Identity**

**7.** $(1)52 = 52$   **Mult. Identity**     **8.** $12 + 5 = 12 + 5$   **Reflexive**

**10. Symmetric**

**11. Substitution**

**9.** $17 + 0 = 17$   **Add. Identity**     **10.** If $6 + 7 = 13$, then $13 = 6 + 7$.

**11.** $(60 - 20) - 10 = 40 - 10$     **12.** If $2^3 = 8$ and $8 = 10 - 2$, then $2^3 = 10 - 2$.   **Transitive**

**Evaluate each expression. Name the property used in each step.**

**13–14. See Teacher's Answer Key.**

**13.** $70 \div 10 + 3(6 - 3 \cdot 2) - 6 \div 2$     **14.** $8(7 - 6) + 48 \div 4^2$

**15. Telecommunications**  A direct-dialed telephone call costs $0.27 for the first minute and $0.11 for each additional minute or fraction of a minute.

**15a.** $0.27 + 6(0.11)$

**15b.** $= 0.27 + 0.66$ **Sub.**
   $= 0.93$   **Sub. (=)**

   **a.** Write an expression that represents the cost of a 7-minute call.

   **b.** Evaluate the expression. Name the property used in each step.

   **c.** How much will the 7-minute call cost?   **$0.93**

# The Distributive Property

When you find the product of two integers, you find the sum of two partial products. For example, you can write

$$\begin{array}{r} 63 \\ \times\ 7 \\ \hline 441 \end{array} \quad \text{as} \quad \begin{array}{r} 60 + 3 \\ \times \qquad 7 \\ \hline 420 + 21 \end{array} \leftarrow (60 \times 7) + (3 \times 7).$$

The statement $(60 + 3) \times 7 = (60 \times 7) + (3 \times 7)$ illustrates the **distributive property**. The multiplier 7 is distributed over the 60 and the 3.

| Distributive Property |
|---|
| For any numbers $a$, $b$, and $c$, $a(b + c) = ab + ac$ and $(b + c)a = ba + ca$; $a(b - c) = ab - ac$ and $(b - c)a = ba - ca$. |

You can use the distributive property to simplify algebraic expressions.

**Example**

Simplify $6(xy + z) + 9z$.

$$\begin{aligned} 6(xy + z) + 9z &= 6xy + 6z + 9z \quad \textit{Distributive property} \\ &= 6xy + (6 + 9)z \quad \textit{Distributive property} \\ &= 6xy + 15z \quad \textit{Substitution } (=) \end{aligned}$$

## EXERCISES

**Name the coefficient of each term. Then name the like terms in each list of terms.**

1. $12r^3, 7r^2, 3r^3, 4r$
   **12, 7, 3, 4; $12r^3$, $3r^3$**

2. $3xy, 11x, 3y, 5x$
   **3, 11, 3, 5; 11x, 5x**

**Use the distributive property to find each product.**

3. $6 \cdot 27$  **162**

4. $4 \cdot 93$  **372**

**Use the distributive property to rewrite each expression.**

5. $7(5w + 3)$  **35w + 21**

6. $5a - 5b$  **5(a − b)**

**Simplify each expression, if possible. If not possible, write in simplest form.**

7. $12c - 5c$  **7c**

8. $6(4x + 9)$  **24x + 54**

9. $2t + 15t + 16y - 9y$

9. **17t + 7y**

10. $26rs + 17st$
    **in simplest form**

11. $2w - 3(4v + 3v)$
    **2w − 21v**

12. $0.9(0.3z - 2) + 0.7z$
    **0.97z − 1.8**

13. **Business** Each month, a business owner pays $23 for telephone service and $9.95 for an on-line service.

   a. Write an expression representing the owner's total costs for telephone and on-line services for an entire year.  **12(23 + 9.95)**

13b. **$395.40**

   b. What amount does the business owner pay for these services for a year?

# Commutative and Associative Properties

The commutative and associative properties can be used to simplify expressions.

| Commutative Properties | For any numbers $a$ and $b$, $a + b = b + a$ and $a \cdot b = b \cdot a$. |
|---|---|
| Associative Properties | For any numbers $a$, $b$, and $c$, $(a + b) + c = a + (b + c)$ and $(ab)c = a(bc)$. |

**Example**

Simplify $4(3m + 5n) + 12m$.

$$
\begin{aligned}
4(3m + 5n) + 12m &= (12m + 20n) + 12m && \textit{Distributive property} \\
&= (20n + 12m) + 12m && \textit{Commutative } (+) \\
&= 20n + (12m + 12m) && \textit{Associative } (+) \\
&= 20n + (12 + 12)m && \textit{Distributive property} \\
&= 20n + 24m && \textit{Substitution } (=)
\end{aligned}
$$

## EXERCISES

**Simplify.**

1. $5a + 6b + 12a$   **$17a + 6b$**

2. $3mn + 14m + 9mn$   **$12mn + 14m$**

3. $5(3q + 2r) + 3(r + 5)$

4. $8x^2 + 9y^2 + 3x^2$   **$11x^2 + 9y^2$**

5. $6st + 9s^2t + 7st$   **$13st + 9s^2t$**

6. $3xy + 5x^2y + 10(3x^2y)$

7. $3(2q + r) - 4q + 6r$   **$2q + 9r$**

8. $0.4(20m + 12n) + 3m$   **$11m + 4.8n$**

9. $\frac{1}{5} + \frac{3}{10}(b + 2) + \frac{3}{5}$   **$\frac{7}{5} + \frac{3}{10}b$**

10. $2(0.9w + 0.3v) + 4w$   **$5.8w + 0.6v$**

11. $0.1(8s + 7t) + 4(s + t)$   **$4.8s + 4.7t$**

12. $\frac{1}{2}c + 3d + \frac{1}{4}c + \frac{1}{2}d$   **$\frac{3}{4}c + \frac{7}{2}d$**

**3. $15q + 13r + 15$**

**6. $3xy + 35x^2y$**

**Name the property illustrated by each statement.**

13. $13a + 4b = 4b + 13a$

14. $2(x + 7) = 2x + 2(7)$

15. $1 \cdot z^4 = z^4$   **Multiplicative Identity**

16. $(5w + 7) + 6z = 5w + (7 + 6z)$

**13. Comm. Prop. (+)**

**14. Distributive Property**

**16. Associative Property (+)**

17. **Automobiles**   Consider the steps necessary to fill your car's gasoline tank. One step is to remove the gasoline tank cap and the other step is to pump the gasoline. Would you say that these steps are commutative?   **No, the order of these steps cannot be reversed.**

# A Preview of Graphs and Functions

Thiel bought a used car with a mileage of 28,000 miles. He drives the car 1500 miles per month. Mathematically, the car's mileage can be defined by the open sentence mileage = $28{,}000 + 1{,}500t$, where $t$ is the length of ownership in months. The table at the right shows the car's mileage over a period of 4 months.

| Length of Ownership | Car's Mileage |
|---|---|
| 0 month | 28,000 |
| 1 month | 29,500 |
| 2 months | 31,000 |
| 3 months | 32,500 |
| 4 months | 34,000 |

This information can also be represented in a graph. The graph shows the relationship between the car's mileage and the length of Thiel's ownership.

You can use a graph without scales on either axis to show the general shape of the graph that represents a situation.

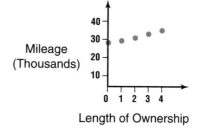

**Example**

In a test of a car's brakes, the car is accelerated on a test track. Then the driver suddenly slams on the brakes to bring the car to a stop. Choose the graph that best represents this situation.

a. 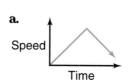   b.    c.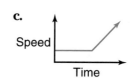

To select the graph that best represents this situation, find the graph that shows an increase in speed, followed by a decrease in speed. Graph a matches this description.

## EXERCISES

1. Identify the graph that matches the following statement. Explain your answer. The outside temperature increases in the morning and falls in the afternoon.  **a**

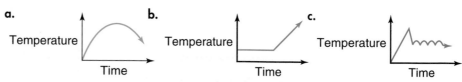

**Sketch a reasonable graph for each situation.**

2–3. See Teacher's Answer Key.

2. Martien is in-line skating at a steady pace. Then she stops to drink some water. After her break, she continues her skating.

3. Tristan likes to trade Olympic pins. He started the week with lots of pins in his collection. Later in the week he lost and sold many of his pins. The next week he began building up his collection again.

times a number and 7.  **3x + 7**

**3x⁵**

## Give the next two items for each pattern.

**3.** 1600, 800, 400, 200, . . .  **100, 50**

**4.** 4, 9, 14, 19, 24, . . .  **29, 34**

## Evaluate each expression.

**5.** $105 - 45 \div 15 + 6$  **108**

**6.** $4^2[(20 - 4) \div 8]$  **32**

**7.** Write the members of the data set used to make the stem-and-leaf plot.
**70, 74, 76, 77, 81, 82, 89, 93, 93, 95, 98**

| Stem | Leaf |
|------|------|
| 7 | 0 4 6 7 |
| 8 | 1 2 9 |
| 9 | 3 3 5 8 |

$8 \,|\, 1 = 81$

**8.** Suppose the number 1816 is rounded to 1820 and plotted using stem 18 and leaf 20. Write the stem and leaf for 1738.  **stem = 17, leaf = 40**

## Solve each equation.

**9.** $q = 7.3 - 5.41$  **1.89**

**10.** $\frac{1}{5} + \frac{3}{10} = r$  **$\frac{1}{2}$**

## State the property illustrated by each statement.

**11.** $5(13 + 2) = 5 \cdot 13 + 5 \cdot 2$  **Distributive**

**12.** $0 + 17 = 17$  **Identity (+)**

**13.** $(9 - 4) + b = 5 + b$  **Substitution**

**14.** $2(st) = (2s)t$  **Assoc. (×)**

**15.** $5 + t = t + 5$  **Commutative (+)**

**16.** If $w = y$ and $y = 4$, then $w = 4$.  **Transitive**

**17.** Simplify $2m + 4(m + 3n)$.  **6m + 12n**

**18.** Identify two ordered pairs on the graph at the right.  **(1990, 5.5), (1991, 6.7)**

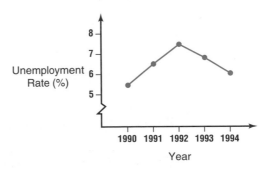

**19.** Sketch a reasonable graph for the following situation.
*Miguel turns on the oven to preheat. He bakes a casserole for 1 hour at 350° F. Then he turns off the oven.*  **See Teacher's Answer Key.**

# Integers and the Number Line

The figure at the right is part of a number line. On a number line, the set of numbers that include 0 and numbers to the right of 0 are named by members of the set of **whole numbers**.

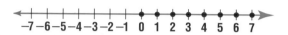

The set of numbers used to name the points marked on the number line at the right is called the set of **integers**.

To graph a set of numbers means to locate the points named by those numbers on the number line. The number that corresponds to a point on the number line is called the **coordinate** of the point.

Name the coordinate of point *K*.

The coordinate of *K* is 3.

A number line is often used to show addition of integers. For example, to find the sum of 4 and −7, follow the steps at the right.

| Step 1 | Draw an arrow, starting at 0 and going to 4. |
|---|---|
| Step 2 | Start at 4. Draw an arrow 7 units to the left. |
| Step 3 | The second arrow points to the sum, −3. |

## EXERCISES

**Name the coordinate of each point.**

1. D **2**  2. B **−7**  3. E **8**  4. C **−3**  5. A **−11**  6. F **12**

**Graph each set of numbers on a number line.**

7–11. See Teacher's Answer Key.

7. {−4, −2, 0, 3}  8. {−5, −1, 2, 5}  9. {−2, −1, 0, . . .}

10. {integers less than 5 but greater than or equal to 0}

11. {integers greater than −4}

**Find each sum. If necessary, use a number line.**

12. −3 + (−9)  **−12**  13. −5 + 7  **2**  14. 12 + (−14)  **−2**

15. −3 + 3  **0**  16. 8 + (−4)  **4**  17. −11 + 3  **−8**

18. **Temperature**  The lowest temperature ever recorded in the state of Arizona was −40°. The highest temperature ever recorded in Arizona was 168° higher. What was the highest temperature ever recorded in Arizona?  **128°**

# Integration: Statistics
# Line Plots

The table below shows the amount Nicole earned each month for babysitting last year. The amounts are recorded in dollars.

| Nicole's Earnings (dollars) | | |
|---|---|---|
| 36 | 45 | 60 |
| 55 | 39 | 57 |
| 45 | 42 | 58 |
| 33 | 45 | 64 |

Numerical information displayed on a number line is called a **line plot**. The line plot below is another way to show the data for Nicole's babysitting earnings.

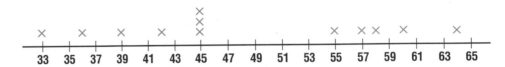

## EXERCISES

1. The largest counties in the United States in 1994 are listed below.

| County | Population |
|---|---|
| Los Angeles, CA | 9,149,840 |
| Cook, IL | 5,141,375 |
| Harris, TX | 3,045,212 |
| San Diego, CA | 2,632,047 |
| Orange, CA | 2,543,124 |
| Maricopa, AZ | 2,346,610 |

a. Make a line plot of the data. **See Teacher's Answer Key.**

b. How many counties have at least 3 million residents? **3 counties**

c. Write a sentence that compares the population of Los Angeles County with the populations of the three smallest counties in the table.

**1c. Los Angeles County has more than three times as many residents as the three smallest counties in the table.**

2. The table below lists the heights of marching band members at McKinley High School.

| Heights of Marching Band Members (inches) | | | | | | | |
|---|---|---|---|---|---|---|---|
| 63 | 67 | 63 | 64 | 62 | 65 | 66 | 64 |
| 72 | 70 | 65 | 69 | 65 | 66 | 68 | |

a. Make a line plot of the data. **See Teacher's Answer Key.**

b. How many band members are taller than 65 inches? **7 members**

c. Which height occurred most frequently? **65 inches**

# Adding and Subtracting Integers

Use the following definitions, rules, and properties when adding or subtracting integers.

| Definition, Rule, or Property | | Example |
|---|---|---|
| **Definition of Absolute Value** | For any real number $a$: if $a > 0$, then $|a| = a$, and if $a < 0$, then $|a| = -a$. | $|6| = 6$ <br> $|-6| = 6$ |
| **Adding Integers with the Same Sign** | To add integers with the same sign, add their absolute values. Give the result the same sign as the integers. | $7 + 8 = 15$ <br> $-7 + (-8) = -15$ |
| **Adding Integers with Different Signs** | To add integers with different signs, subtract the lesser absolute value from the greater absolute value. Give the result the same sign as the integer with the greater absolute value. | $-10 + 3 = -7$ <br> $6 + (-2) = 4$ |
| **Additive Inverse Property** | For every number $a$, $a + (-a) = 0$. | $-5 + 5 = 0$ |
| **Subtracting Integers** | To subtract a number, add its additive inverse. For any numbers $a$ and $b$, $a - b = a + (-b)$. | $13 - (-8) = 13 + 8$ <br> $= 21$ |

You can use the distributive property and the addition and subtraction rules for integers to simplify expressions with like terms.

**Example**  ● **Simplify $-3w - 2w + 10w$.**

$$-3w - 2w + 10w = -3w + (-2w) + 10w$$
$$= [-3 + (-2) + 10]w$$
$$= (-5 + 10)w$$
$$= 5w$$

## EXERCISES

**Find each sum or difference.**

1. $-13 + (-7)$  **−20**
2. $96 + (-54)$  **42**
3. $39 + 62$  **101**
4. $18 - 32$  **−14**
5. $26 - (-40)$  **66**
6. $-27 - (-14)$  **−13**
7. $12a + (-17a) - 4a$
8. $-2t + 20t + (-7t)$
9. $-6x + 15x - (-20x)$

7. **−9a**
8. **11t**
9. **29x**
10. **215**
11. **−25**
12. **−36**
13. **11**

**Evaluate each expression if $a = 2$, $b = -3$, and $c = -1$.**

10. $212 + |b|$
11. $b + (-23) + |c|$
12. $-34 - |a|$
13. $16 - a - |b|$

14. **Elevators**  The World Trade Center building in New York City has 110 stories. If an employee rode the elevator to her office on the 83rd floor, then came down 35 floors to deliver a report, which floor is she on now?  **48th floor**

# Rational Numbers

| Definition of a Rational Number | A rational number is a number that can be expressed in the form $\frac{a}{b}$, where $a$ and $b$ are integers and $b$ is not equal to 0. |
|---|---|

You can compare rational numbers by graphing them on a number line.

| Comparing Numbers on the Number Line | If $a$ and $b$ represent any numbers and the graph of $a$ is to the left of the graph of $b$, then $a < b$. If the graph of $a$ is to the right of the graph of $b$, then $a > b$. |
|---|---|
| Comparison Property | For any two numbers $a$ and $b$, exactly one of the following sentences is true: $a < b$, $a = b$, or $a > b$. |

**Example 1**  
a. $-5\frac{1}{3} < -2\frac{1}{3}$  The graph of $-5\frac{1}{3}$ is to the left of the graph of $-2\frac{1}{3}$.

b. $-1\frac{1}{8} > -4\frac{3}{8}$  The graph of $-1\frac{1}{8}$ is to the right of the graph of $-4\frac{4}{5}$.

**Example 2**  Replace __?__ with $<$, $>$, or $=$ to make the sentence true.

$-9$ __?__ $-11$

$-9 > -11$  Since $-9$ is to the right of $-11$ on a number line, $-9$ is greater than $-11$.

You can use **cross products** to compare two fractions with different denominators.

| Comparison Property for Rational Numbers | For any rational numbers $\frac{a}{b}$ and $\frac{c}{d}$, with $b > 0$ and $d > 0$: <br> 1. if $\frac{a}{b} < \frac{c}{d}$, then $ad < bc$, and <br> 2. if $ad < bc$, then $\frac{a}{b} < \frac{c}{d}$. |
|---|---|

*This property also holds if $<$ is replaced by $>$, $\leq$, $\geq$, or $=$.*

## EXERCISES

**Replace each __?__ with $<$, $>$, or $=$ to make each sentence true.**

1. $-6$ __?__ $3$  **<**  2. $-2$ __?__ $-17 + 12$  **>**  3. $-3 - 4$ __?__ $-16 + 9$  **=**

**Write the numbers in each set in order from least to greatest.**

4. $-\frac{1}{5}, 0.3, -2.5$  **$-2.5, -\frac{1}{5}, 0.3$**  5. $\frac{1}{8}, -1, -\frac{9}{7}$  **$-\frac{9}{7}, -1, \frac{1}{8}$**

6. Find a number between $\frac{1}{3}$ and $\frac{7}{15}$.  **Sample answer: $\frac{5}{12}$**

7. Which is the better buy? A 15-ounce box of cereal for \$1.99 or a 20-ounce box of cereal for \$2.49?  **20-ounce box**

# Adding and Subtracting Rational Numbers

The rules for adding and subtracting integers also apply to adding and subtracting rational numbers.

| Rational Number | Form $\frac{a}{b}$ |
|---|---|
| 5 | $\frac{5}{1}$ |
| $-1\frac{2}{3}$ | $-\frac{5}{3}$ |
| 0.75 | $\frac{3}{4}$ |

**Example ❶**

**a.** Find $\left(-3\frac{1}{4}\right) + 6\frac{1}{2}$.

$$\left(-3\tfrac{1}{4}\right) + 6\tfrac{1}{2} = +\left(\left|6\tfrac{2}{4}\right| - \left|-3\tfrac{1}{4}\right|\right)$$

$$= +\left(6\tfrac{2}{4} - 3\tfrac{1}{4}\right)$$

$$= 3\tfrac{1}{4}$$

**b.** Find $-6.14 - 9.87$.

$$-6.14 - 9.87 = -6.14 + (-9.87)$$

$$= -16.01$$

To add three or more numbers, first group the numbers in pairs. Use the commutative and associative properties to rearrange the addends if necessary. Study the example below.

**Example ❷**

Find $-\frac{1}{4} + \frac{5}{6} + \left(-\frac{7}{4}\right)$.

$$-\tfrac{1}{4} + \tfrac{5}{6} + \left(-\tfrac{7}{4}\right) = \left[-\tfrac{1}{4} + \left(-\tfrac{7}{4}\right)\right] + \tfrac{5}{6}$$

$$= -\tfrac{8}{4} + \tfrac{5}{6}$$

$$= -\tfrac{24}{12} + \tfrac{10}{12}$$

$$= -\tfrac{14}{12} \text{ or } -1\tfrac{1}{6}$$

## EXERCISES

**Find each sum or difference.**

1. $-\frac{4}{13} + \left(-\frac{7}{13}\right)$   $-\frac{11}{13}$    2. $\frac{3}{4} + \left(-\frac{7}{8}\right)$   $-\frac{1}{8}$    3. $-0.019 + 0.062$   **0.043**

4. $\frac{4}{7} - \left(-\frac{2}{7}\right)$   $\frac{6}{7}$      5. $3.97 - 1.55$   **2.42**    6. $-\frac{2}{3} - \frac{4}{9}$   $-\frac{10}{9}$

**Evaluate each expression if $a = -0.25$ and $b = \frac{1}{3}$.**

9. $-2.75$

11. $1.8$

12. $-36q$

7. $a + 0.53$   **0.28**    8. $2 - b$   $\frac{5}{3}$     9. $-3 - a$      10. $b + \frac{2}{7}$   $\frac{13}{21}$

**Find each sum.**

11. $-44.1 + 62.7 + (-16.8)$    12. $-13q + (-41q) + 18q$    13. $\frac{1}{4} + \left(-\frac{3}{8}\right) + \frac{1}{2}$   $\frac{3}{8}$

14. **Fishing** The saltwater fish record for redeye bass is 8.75 pounds. The record for black sea bass is 0.75 pounds more than the redeye bass record. The record for barred sand bass is 3.75 pounds more than the black sea bass record. What is the record for barred sand bass?   **13.25 pounds**

# Multiplying Rational Numbers

You can use the rules below when multiplying rational numbers.

| Rule or Property | | Example |
|---|---|---|
| **Multiplying Two Numbers with Different Signs** | The product of two numbers that have different signs is negative. | $(-3m)9n = (-3)(9)mn$ $= -27mn$ |
| **Multiplying Two Numbers with the Same Sign** | The product of two numbers that have the same sign is positive. | $(-11)(-4) = 44$ |
| **Multiplicative Property of $-1$** | The product of any number and $-1$ is its additive inverse. $-1(a) = -a$ and $a(-1) = -a$ | $(-2)(-7)(-1)(5) = 14(-1)(5)$ $= -14(5)$ $= -70$ |

To find the product of two or more numbers, first group the numbers in pairs.

**Example** ● Find $(-3.1)(7.4)(-0.1)(-0.5)$.

$(-3.1)(7.4)(-0.1)(-0.5) = [(-3.1)(7.4)]\,[(-0.1)(-0.5)]$  *Associative* $(\times)$

$= (-22.94)(0.05)$  *Substitution* $(=)$

$- -1.147$

## EXERCISES

**Find each product.**

1. $(-18)(-3)$ **54**

2. $(10.0)(-0.14)$ **−1.4**

3. $(-1)(-5)(-3)$ **−15**

4. $\left(\frac{1}{4}\right)(-16)(12)$ **−48**

5. $(-4)(-55)\left(-\frac{3}{5}\right)$ **−132**

6. $\left(\frac{5}{6}\right)(-2)(-1)(-3)$ **−5**

**Simplify.**

7. $(-7)(2) + (3)(6)$ **4**

8. $\left(-\frac{1}{3}\right)\left(\frac{3}{5}\right) - \left(\frac{1}{2}\right)\left(\frac{1}{5}\right)$ **$-\frac{3}{10}$**

9. −9s − 4st

9. $-3(5s - 2s) + 4(-st)$

10. $(-9mn)4 - mn(7 - 5)$ **−38mn**

11. 28x − 24.4y

11. $6.2(5x - 2y) - 1.5(2x + 8y)$

12. $(-8)(3) - (-4)(6)$ **0**

13. **Nutrition** The recommended daily allowance (RDA) of calcium for a teenaged female is 1200 mg. An eight-ounce serving of skim milk contains 302 mg of calcium. A one-ounce serving of cheddar cheese contains 204 mg of calcium. A medium orange contains 52 mg of calcium.

a. How much calcium is in 3 eight-ounce servings of skim milk? **906 mg**

13b. No, 906 mg is less than 1200 mg.

b. Do 3 eight-ounce servings of skim milk satisfy the RDA of calcium for a teenaged female? Explain your reasoning.

13c. Yes, 204 + 2(52) + 906 = 1214, which is greater than 1200.

c. Would a serving of cheddar cheese and 2 oranges, in addition to 3 servings of skim milk, satisfy the RDA of calcium for a teenaged female? Explain your reasoning.

# Dividing Rational Numbers

Use the following rules to divide rational numbers.

| Rule or Property | | Example |
|---|---|---|
| **Dividing Two Rational Numbers** | The quotient of two numbers having the same sign is positive. The quotient of two numbers having different signs is negative. | $-40 \div (-8) = 5$ $-63 \div 7 = -9$ |
| **Multiplicative Inverse Property** | For every nonzero number $\frac{a}{b}$, where $a, b \neq 0$, there is exactly one number $\frac{b}{a}$ such that $\frac{a}{b} \cdot \frac{b}{a} = 1$. | $\frac{3}{8} \cdot \frac{8}{3} = 1$ $-\frac{2}{5} \cdot -\frac{5}{2} = 1$ |
| **Division Rule** | For all numbers $a$ and $b$, with $b \neq 0$, $a \div b = \frac{a}{b} = a\left(\frac{1}{b}\right) = \frac{1}{b}(a)$. | $15 \div 3 = \frac{15}{3}$ $= 15\left(\frac{1}{3}\right)$ $= \frac{1}{3}(15)$ |

Since the fraction bar indicates division, you can use the division rules and the distributive property to simplify rational expressions.

**Example**  **Simplify** $\frac{-42p + 18}{6}$.

$$\frac{-42p + 18}{6} = (-42p + 18)\left(\frac{1}{6}\right)$$
$$= (-42p)\left(\frac{1}{6}\right) + 18\left(\frac{1}{6}\right)$$
$$= -7p + 3$$

## EXERCISES

**Simplify.**

1. $-\frac{54q}{9}$  $-6q$

2. $\frac{48t}{16}$  $3t$

3. $\frac{120}{24}$  $5$

4. $\frac{45}{-15}$  $-3$

5. $\frac{-78y}{3}$  $-26y$

6. $\frac{-96}{-37} \div \frac{96}{37}$  $1$

7. $\frac{52w}{13}$  $4w$

8. $-\frac{1}{5} \div 5$  $-\frac{1}{25}$

9. $\frac{24d - 16c}{-4}$  $-6d + 4c$

10. $27s^2 + 3stu$

10. $\frac{18s}{2} \div \frac{1}{3s} + 3stu$

11. $\frac{44x - 28}{4}$  $11x - 7$

12. $\frac{-\frac{3}{7}}{3}$  $-\frac{1}{7}$

13. **Cooking**  Theo has a recipe for chocolate chip cookies that makes 6 dozen cookies. He only has enough flour to make 3 dozen cookies.

13a. $1\frac{1}{8}$ cups

  a. If the original recipe calls for $2\frac{1}{4}$ cups of margarine, how much margarine will he need to make 3 dozen cookies?

13b. $1\frac{3}{4}$ teaspoons

  b. If the original recipe calls for $3\frac{1}{2}$ teaspoons of baking powder, how much baking powder will he need to make 3 dozen cookies?

# Square Roots and Real Numbers

| Counting or Natural Numbers, N | {1, 2, 3, 4, . . . } |
| --- | --- |
| Whole Numbers, W | {0, 1, 2, 3, 4, . . . } |
| Integers, Z | { . . . , −3, −2, −1, 0, 1, 2, 3, . . . } |
| Rational Numbers, Q | {all numbers that can be expressed in the form $\frac{a}{b}$, where $a$ and $b$ are integers and $b \neq 0$} |
| Irrational Numbers, I | {numbers that cannot be expressed in the form $\frac{a}{b}$, where $a$ and $b$ are integers and $b \neq 0$} |
| Real Numbers, R | {rational numbers and irrational numbers} |

A **square root** is one of two equal factors of a number. For example, the square root of 49 is 7 and −7 since 7 · 7 is 49 and (−7)(−7) is also 49. Since the square root of 49 is a rational number, it is a **perfect square**.

The symbol $\sqrt{\ }$ is called a **radical sign**. It indicates the nonnegative, or **principal**, square root of the expression under the radical sign.

**Example**  Find $\pm\sqrt{25}$.  The symbol $\pm\sqrt{25}$ represents both square roots. Since $5^2 = 25$, we know that $\pm\sqrt{25} = \pm5$.

Numbers such as $\sqrt{2}$ and $\sqrt{3}$ are not perfect squares. Notice what happens when you find these square roots with your calculator. These numbers are not rational numbers since they are not repeating or terminating decimals. They are classified as **irrational numbers**.

## EXERCISES

**Find each square root. Use a calculator if necessary. Round to the nearest hundredth if the result is not a whole number.**

1. $\sqrt{64}$    2. $\sqrt{0.00036}$    3. $-\sqrt{\frac{81}{49}}$    4. $-\sqrt{2500}$    5. $\pm\sqrt{\frac{144}{25}}$

**Evaluate each expression. Use a calculator if necessary. Round to the nearest hundredth if the result is not a whole number.**

6. $\sqrt{y}$, if $y = 76$   **8.72**       7. $\pm\sqrt{c + d}$, if $c = 14$ and $d = 45$

**Name the set or sets of numbers to which each real number belongs. Use N for natural numbers, W for whole numbers, Z for integers, Q for rational numbers, and I for irrational numbers.**

8. $\sqrt{24}$  **I**         9. 7.8  **Q**        10. $\sqrt{100}$  **N, W, Z, Q**

11. **Aviation**  The formula to determine the distance $d$ in miles that an object can be seen on a clear day on the surface of the ocean is $d = 1.4\sqrt{h}$, where $h$ is the height in feet the viewer's eyes are above the surface of the water. About how many miles can the pilot of an airplane see if the airplane is 2000 feet above the water?  **62.6 miles**

1. 8
2. 0.02
3. $-\frac{9}{7}$
4. −50
5. $\pm\frac{12}{5}$
7. ±7.68

# Problem Solving
# Write Equations and Formulas

When solving a problem, you should read and explore the problem until you completely understand the relationships in the given information. Then you may translate the problem into an equation or formula. In an equation, you choose a variable to represent one of the unspecified numbers in the problem. This is called **defining the variable**. Then use the variable to write expressions for the other unspecified numbers in the problem. In a formula, an equation that states a rule for the relationship between certain quantities is formed.

---

**Problem-Solving Plan**

1. Explore the problem.
2. Plan the solution.
3. Solve the problem.
4. Examine the solution.

---

## EXERCISES

**Answer the related questions for the verbal problems below.**

1. Will can mow a lawn in 3 hours. Tazeen can mow the same lawn in 2 hours.

   a. How much of the lawn can Will mow in one hour?   $\frac{1}{3}$

   b. How much of the lawn can Tazeen mow in one hour?   $\frac{1}{2}$

2. An airplane can hold a maximum of 120 people. The airplane is two-thirds full. One-fourth of the passengers remain on the airplane when it lands at the end of the first leg of its flight.

   a. How many people are on the airplane on the first leg of its flight?   **80**

   b. How many people remain on the airplane when it lands?   **20**

**Translate each sentence into an equation, an inequality, or formula.**

3. The area of a square is the length $s$ of its side squared.   $A = s^2$

4. Two-thirds of the sum of $m$ and $n$ is 71.   $\frac{2}{3}(m + n) = 71$

5. The product of $x$ and $y$ is greater than 7 times the sum of $x$ and $y$.
   $xy > 7(x + y)$

**Define a variable, then write an equation for each problem. Do *not* try to solve.   6–7. See Teacher's Answer Key.**

6. One number is 65 less than a second number. The sum of the two numbers is 192. Find the numbers.

7. Andra has 90 books. If she has 10 more than one-third as many paperbacks as hardbacks, how many paperbacks does Andra have?

1. Graph $\{-3, -1, 0, 2, 5\}$ on a number line.   **See Teacher's Answer Key.**

2. Name the coordinate of point $P$.   **−2**

**Use the table below for Exercises 3–4.**

| Biology Test Scores | | | | |
|---|---|---|---|---|
| 88 | 85 | 91 | 98 | 83 |
| 91 | 89 | 92 | 95 | 71 |
| 74 | 82 | 84 | 79 | 86 |

3. Make a line plot representing the scores on a biology test.   **See Teacher's Answer Key.**

4. How many scores were 90 or above?   **5**

**Find each sum or difference.**

5. $-94 + 36$   **−58**

6. $13.1 + (-5.6) + (-6.2) + 0.89$   **2.19**

7. $\frac{1}{8} + \left(-\frac{3}{16}\right)$   **$-\frac{1}{16}$**

8. $4 - 13$   **−9**

9. Find the value of $|y - x|$ if $x = 2$ and $y = -3$.   **5**

10. Write $-\frac{3}{4}, 0.9, -1.4, 1.1$ in order from least to greatest.   **$-1.4, -\frac{3}{4}, 0.9, 1.1$**

**Simplify.**

11. $(-9)(4) + (2)(11)$   **−14**

12. $3.1(2x - 3y) - 4.5(8x + 2y)$   **$-29.8x - 18.3y$**

13. $\frac{-63q}{9}$   **−7q**

14. $\frac{-51}{-17} \div \frac{102}{34}$   **1**

15. $-\sqrt{\frac{64}{9}}$   **$-\frac{8}{3}$**

16. $\sqrt{55 - 6}$   **7**

17. Translate the following sentence into an equation.
Twice the sum of $a$ and $b$ is 46.   **$2(a + b) = 46$**

18. Define a variable, then write an equation for the following. Do *not* try to solve.
One number is 61 more than a second number. The sum of the two numbers is 127. Find the numbers.

**Let $x$ = one number, then
$x + 61$ = the other number;
$x + (x + 61) = 127$.**

# Solving Equations with Addition and Subtraction

You can use the addition and subtraction properties of equality to solve equations. To check, substitute the solution for the variable in the original equation. If the resulting sentence is true, your solution is correct.

| Addition Property of Equality | For any numbers $a$, $b$, and $c$, if $a = b$, then $a + c = b + c$. |
|---|---|
| Subtraction Property of Equality | For any numbers $a$, $b$, and $c$, if $a = b$, then $a - c = b - c$. |

**Example 1** Solve $z - 15 = -3$.

$$z - 15 = -3$$
$$z - 15 + 15 = -3 + 15$$
$$z = 12$$

**Check:** $z - 15 = -3$
$$12 - 15 \stackrel{?}{=} -3$$
$$-3 = -3 \checkmark$$

**Example 2** Solve $q + 5 = -2$.

$$q + 5 = -2$$
$$q + 5 - 5 = -2 - 5$$
$$q = -7$$

**Check:** $q + 5 = -2$
$$-7 + 5 \stackrel{?}{=} -2$$
$$-2 = -2 \checkmark$$

Sometimes an equation can be solved more easily if it is rewritten first. Recall that subtracting a number is the same as adding its inverse. For example, the equation $b - (-3) = 11$ may be rewritten as $b + 3 = 11$.

## EXERCISES

**Solve each equation. Then check your solution.**

1. $w - 7 = -34$  **−27**
2. $y + 8 = 3$  **−5**
3. $q + 5 = -20$  **−25**
4. $-6 = m + 3$  **−9**
5. $d + (-12) = 4$  **16**
6. $t - (-23) = 14$  **−9**
7. $16 + a = -11$  **−27**
8. $62 = 41 - s$  **−21**
9. $-7.4 = c + (-1.6)$
10. $-32 - x = 22\frac{5}{8}$
11. $-\frac{1}{6} + b = \frac{2}{3}$  **$\frac{5}{6}$**
12. $\frac{4}{11} = -n + \frac{1}{3}$  **$-\frac{1}{33}$**

9. **−5.8**
10. **$-54\frac{5}{8}$**

13. **Clothing Design** A clothing designer is designing a blazer. The blazer will have three buttons on the front. The length of each button hole is to be $\frac{1}{8}$-inch longer than the sum of the diameter and the thickness of the button.
   a. Translate the description of the button hole length into a formula.
   b. Suppose the clothing designer decides that each button hole is to be $\frac{15}{16}$-inch long and each button is to be $\frac{5}{8}$-inch in diameter. What thickness should the button be?

13a. $\ell = \frac{1}{8} + (d + t)$
13b. $\frac{3}{16}$ inch

# Solving Equations with Multiplication and Division

You can solve equations in which a variable has a coefficient by using the multiplication and division properties of equality.

| Multiplication Property of Equality | For any numbers $a$, $b$, and $c$, if $a = b$, then $ac = bc$. |
|---|---|
| Division Property of Equality | For any numbers $a$, $b$, and $c$, with $c \neq 0$, if $a = b$, then $\frac{a}{c} = \frac{b}{c}$. |

**Example**  Solve $\frac{1}{7}p = 3$.

$$\frac{1}{7}p = 3$$
$$7\left(\frac{1}{7}p\right) = 7(3)$$
$$p = 21$$

**Check:** $\frac{1}{7}p = 3$
$$\frac{1}{7}(21) \overset{?}{=} 3$$
$$3 = 3 \checkmark$$

**Example**  Solve $4x = 28$.

$$4x = 28$$
$$\frac{4x}{4} = \frac{28}{4}$$
$$x = 7$$

**Check:** $4x = 28$
$$4(7) \overset{?}{=} 28$$
$$28 = 28 \checkmark$$

# EXERCISES

**Solve each equation. Then check your solution.**

1. $-6z = -72$   **12**
2. $-4q = 48$   **−12**
3. $5r = -35$   **−7**
4. $\frac{1}{7}a = -3$   **−21**
5. $8s = \frac{4}{7}$   **$\frac{1}{14}$**
6. $1\frac{1}{3}t = -2\frac{2}{3}$   **−2**

**Define a variable, write an equation, and solve each problem. Then check your solution.**

8. $\frac{1}{3}n = 12$; 36

7. Seven times a number is 63. What is the number?   **$7n = 63$; 9**

8. One third of a number is twelve. What is the number?

9. Negative three times a number is −93. What is the number?   **$-3n = -93$; 31**

10. Tyrone paid $82.50 for 3 ballet tickets. What is the cost of each ticket?   **$3t = 82.50$; $27.50**

**Complete.**

13. 11.25

14. 66

11. If $5y = 80$, then $7y =$ ___.   **112**

12. If $-3r = 27$, then $4r =$ ___.   **−36**

13. If $8b = -45$, then $-2b =$ ___.

14. If $3m - 2n = 33$, then $6m - 4n =$ ___.

# Solving Multi-Step Equations

When solving some equations you must perform more than one operation on both sides. First, determine what operations have been done to the variable. Then undo these operations in the reverse order.

**Example** ❶ How would you solve $\frac{1}{4} + 5 = 13$?

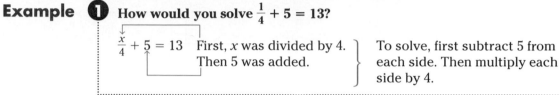

$\frac{x}{4} + 5 = 13$  First, $x$ was divided by 4. Then 5 was added. | To solve, first subtract 5 from each side. Then multiply each side by 4.

---

**Procedure for Solving a Two-Step Equation**

1. Undo any indicated additions or subtractions.
2. Undo any indicated multiplications or divisions involving the variable.

---

**Example** ❷

| | | **Check:** |
|---|---|---|
| $3w + 7 = 34$ | *Addition of 7 is indicated.* | |
| $3w + 7 - 7 = 34 - 7$ | *Therefore, subtract 7 from each side.* | $3w + 7 = 34$ |
| $3w = 27$ | *Multiplication by 3 is also indicated.* | $3(9) + 7 = 34$ |
| $\frac{3w}{3} = \frac{27}{3}$ | *Therefore, divide each side by 3.* | $27 + 7 = 34$ |
| $w = 9$ | | $34 = 34$ ✔ |

## EXERCISES

**Solve each equation. Then check your solution.**

1. $5r - 21 = 44$  **13**
2. $6y + 2 = 50$  **8**
3. $0.9a - 2.6 = 3.7$  **7**
4. $\frac{3m + 15}{2} = 22.5$  **10**
5. $21 = \frac{q + 35}{8}$  **133**
6. $14 + \frac{4z}{-11} = 66$  **−143**
7. $\frac{3}{5}c - 6 = 9$  **25**
8. $\frac{t}{-2} + 17 = -9$  **52**
9. $-6 = \frac{5p - (-2)}{-7}$  **8**

**Define a variable, write an equation, and solve each problem. Then check your solution.**

10. Find three consecutive integers whose sum is 126.

11. Find two consecutive odd integers whose sum is 76.

12. Deborah, Travis, and Tito were each born in one of three consecutive years. The sum of their ages is 45. What are the three ages?

10. $n + (n + 1) + (n + 2) = 126$; 41, 42, 43

11. $n + (n + 2) = 76$; 37, 39

12. $n + (n + 1) + (n + 2) = 45$; 14, 15, and 16 years old

# Integration: Geometry
# Angles and Triangles

| Supplementary Angles | Two angles are supplementary if the sum of their measures is 180°. |
|---|---|
| Complementary Angles | Two angles are complementary if the sum of their measures is 90°. |
| Sum of the Angles of a Triangle | The sum of the measures of the angles in any triangle is 180°. |

**Example** ❶ **The measure of an angle is four times the measure of its supplement. Find the measure of each angle.**

Let $a$ = the lesser measure. Then $4a$ = the greater measure.

$a + 4a = 180$    *The sum of the measures is 180°.*

$5a = 180$    *Add a and 4a.*

$\dfrac{5a}{5} = \dfrac{180}{5}$    *Divide each side by 5.*

$a = 36$    The measures are 36° and 4 · 36° or 144°.

**Example** ❷ **The measures of two angles of a triangle are 42° and 83°. Find the measure of the third angle.**

Let $x$ = the measure of the third angle.

$42 + 83 + x = 180$    *The sum of the measures of the angles is 180°.*

$125 + x = 180$    *Add 42 and 83.*

$125 - 125 + x = 180 - 125$    *Subtract 125 from each side.*

$x = 55$    The measure of the third angle is 55°.

## EXERCISES

**Find both the complement and the supplement of each measure.**

1. 71°   **19; 109°**      2. 48°   **42°; 132°**      3. 25°   **65°; 155°**

4. $(90 - w)°$; $(180 - w)°$      4. $w°$

5. $(76 - y)°$; $(166 - y)°$      5. $(y + 14)°$

6. $(70 + q)°$; $(160 + q)°$      6. $(20 - q)°$

**Find the measure of the third angle of each triangle in which the measures of two angles of the triangle are given.**

7. 110°, 60°   **10°**      8. 70°, 70°   **40°**      9. $x°, 2x°$   **$(180 - 3x)°$**

**Write an equation and solve. Then check your solution.**

10. The measure of an angle is 22° less than its complement. Find the measure of each angle.   **34°, 56°**

11. One of two supplementary angles is 42° more than five times the other. Find the measure of each angle.   **23°, 157°**

12. **Construction**   A freeway exit ramp makes a 4° angle with the horizontal. What is the measure of the angle that the ramp makes with the vertical?   **86°**

# Solving Equations with the Variable on Both Sides

When an equation contains parentheses or other grouping symbols, first use the distributive property to remove the grouping symbols. If the equation has variables on each side, use the addition or subtraction property of equality to write an equivalent equation that has all the variables on one side. Then solve the equation.

**Example**

Solve $6(3z - 4) = -5(z - 14) - 2$.

$$6(3z - 4) = -5(z - 14) - 2$$
$$18z - 24 = -5z + 70 - 2 \qquad \text{\textit{Use the distributive property.}}$$
$$18z + 5z - 24 = -5z + 5z + 70 - 2 \qquad \text{\textit{Add 5z to each side.}}$$
$$23z - 24 = 68$$
$$23z - 24 + 24 = 68 + 24 \qquad \text{\textit{Add 24 to each side.}}$$
$$23z = 92$$
$$\frac{23z}{23} = \frac{92}{23} \qquad \text{\textit{Divide each side by 23.}}$$
$$z = 4$$

**Check:**
$$6(3z - 4) = -5(z - 14) - 2$$
$$6(3 \cdot 4 - 4) \overset{?}{=} -5(4 - 14) - 2$$
$$6(12 - 4) \overset{?}{=} -5(-10) - 2$$
$$6(8) \overset{?}{=} 50 - 2$$
$$48 = 48 \quad ✔$$

Some equations may have *no solution,* and some equations may have *every number* in their solution set. An equation that is true for every value of the variable is called an **identity**.

## EXERCISES

**Solve each equation. Then check your solution.**

1. $-7(b + 16) = 7(b - 4)$  **−6**
2. $9 - z = 3z + 39$  **$-\dfrac{15}{2}$**
3. $12c - 5c = 4c + 15$  **5**
4. $40 - 5s = -2(-1 + 3s)$  **−38**
5. $2.8w + 5.3 = 3.3w - 0.7$  **12**
6. $4(m + 9) = 3(8 - m)$  **$-\dfrac{12}{7}$**
7. $\frac{1}{8}k + 32 = \frac{1}{2}k - 1$  **88**
8. $\frac{3}{4}x - x = -\frac{1}{4}(2x + 10)$  **−10**
9. $7(t + 1) = 5(t - 4) - 1$  **−14**
10. $3d + 1.1 = 2.3 - d$  **0.3**
11. $-7(a + 2) + 15 = 1 - 7a$  **identity**
12. $6(3n - 1) = 2(9n + 4)$  **no solution**

13. **Sales**  Rundell owns a chain of coffee shops. His shops sell both doughnuts and bagels. Over the past few years he has found that the sales of doughnuts have been decreasing by 0.01 million dollars per year, and sales of bagels have been increasing by 0.06 million dollars per year. Last year, Rundell's shops sold 1.6 million dollars in doughnuts and 0.9 million dollars in bagels. If the sales trends continue, after how many years will sales of bagels and doughnuts be equal?  **10 years**

# Solving Equations and Formulas

If an equation that contains more than one variable is to be solved for a specific variable, use the properties of equality to isolate the specified variable on one side of the equation.

**Example**  Solve $5s + t^2 = u - v$ for $s$.

$$5s + t^2 = u - v$$
$$5s + t^2 - t^2 = u - v - t^2 \quad \textit{Subtract } t^2 \textit{ from each side.}$$
$$5s = u - v - t^2$$
$$\frac{5s}{5} = \frac{u - v - t^2}{5} \quad \textit{Divide each side by 5.}$$
$$s = \frac{u - v - t^2}{5}$$

**Example**  Solve $by = abx + cx - c$ for $x$.

$$by = abx + cx - c$$
$$by + c = abx + cx - c + c \quad \textit{Add c to each side.}$$
$$by + c = abx + cx$$
$$by + c = x(ab + c) \quad\quad \textit{Distributive property}$$
$$\frac{by + c}{ab + c} = \frac{x(ab + c)}{ab + c} \quad \textit{Divide each side by } (ab + c).$$
$$\frac{by + c}{ab + c} = x$$

## EXERCISES

**Solve for $y$.**

1. $6 - 2y = z$ $\quad y = \dfrac{6 - z}{2}$

2. $y + 12q = 15$ $\quad y = 15 - 12q$

3. $(y + b) + 14 = 20$ $\quad y = 6 - b$

4. $ay + c = 4$ $\quad y = \dfrac{4 - c}{a}, a \neq 0$

5. $y(3 + m) = 9n$ $\quad y = \dfrac{9n}{3 + m}, m \neq -3$

6. $2g + 5y = 8$ $\quad y = \dfrac{8 - 2g}{5}$

7. $4y + s = t$ $\quad y = \dfrac{t - s}{4}$

8. $y(7 - d) = x$ $\quad y = \dfrac{x}{7 - d}, d \neq 7$

9. $8y - 3v = 5u$ $\quad y = \dfrac{5u + 3v}{8}$

10. $\dfrac{b - y}{5} = a$ $\quad y = b - 5a$

11. **Business** The formula $I = prt$ is the formula for computing simple interest, where I is the interest, $p$ is the principal or the amount invested, $r$ is the interest rate, and $t$ is the time in years. Find the amount of interest earned if you were to invest $8000 at 4% interest (use 0.04) for 5 years. **$1600**

# Integration: Statistics
# Measures of Central Tendency

In working with statistical data, it is often useful to have one value represent the complete set of data. For example, **measures of central tendency** represent centralized values of the data. Three measures of central tendency are the **mean**, **median**, and **mode**.

| | Definitions | Examples |
|---|---|---|
| **Mean** | The mean of a set of data is the sum of the numbers in the set divided by the number of numbers in the set. | Data: 14, 16, 17, 14, 22, 22 $\frac{14 + 16 + 17 + 14 + 22 + 22}{6} = 17.5$ |
| **Median** | The median of a set of data is the middle number when the numbers in the set are arranged in numerical order. In an even number of elements, the median is halfway between the two middle numbers. | Data: 14, 14, 16, 17, 22, 22 $\frac{16 + 17}{2} = 16.5$ |
| **Mode** | The mode of a set of data is the number that occurs most often in the set. | Data: 14, 16, 17, 14, 22, 22 There are two modes, 14 and 22. |

## EXERCISES

**Find the mean, median, and mode(s) for each set of data.**

1. 90, 88, 93, 87, 95

   **90.6; 90; none**

2.

   **2.6; 2.5; 3**

3. 14; 14; 10 and 18

3. 10, 18, 18, 18, 10, 10

4. 12, 7, 14, 30   **15.75; 13; none**

6. 15.2; 12.4; none

5. $\frac{3}{4}, \frac{2}{3}, \frac{3}{5}, \frac{6}{8}$   $\frac{83}{120}; \frac{17}{24}; \frac{3}{4}$

6. 12.4, 6.8, 19.1, 30.4, 7.3

**Find the median and mode(s) of the data shown in each stem-and-leaf plot.**

7.
| Stem | Leaf |
|---|---|
| 5 | 3 8 8 9 |
| 6 | 1 2 2 2 4 6 |
| 7 | 7 7 7 8 9 9 |

$6|2 = 62$   **63; 62 and 77**

8.
| Stem | Leaf |
|---|---|
| 11 | 1 3 4 5 |
| 12 | 2 2 4 4 |
| 13 | 1 3 3 3 4 5 |

$13|3 = 133$   **124; 133**

9. **Football**   The table at the right shows the teams that have played in the Super Bowl most often.

   a. Find the mean, median, and mode of the data.   **5; 5; 5**

   9b. They all represent the data equally well because they are all the same value.

   b. Which measure of central tendency best represents these data, and why?

| Team | Times in Super Bowl |
|---|---|
| Dallas Cowboys | 8 |
| Miami Dolphins | 5 |
| Pittsburgh Steelers | 5 |
| San Francisco 49ers | 5 |
| Washington Redskins | 5 |
| Buffalo Bills | 4 |
| Denver Broncos | 4 |
| Minnesota Vikings | 4 |

**Solve each equation. Then check your solution.**

1. $r - 4 = -48$  **−44**

2. $h + (-9) = 13$  **22**

3. $-\frac{1}{3} + a = \frac{4}{5}$  **$\frac{17}{15}$**

4. $-3z = -39$  **13**

5. $7w = -42$  **−6**

6. $\frac{1}{8}x = -5$  **−40**

7. $11y + 9 = 64$  **5**

8. $34 = \frac{q + 17}{5}$  **153**

9. $\frac{3}{7}c + 3 = 9$  **14**

10. $-3(b + 8) = 3(b - 1)$  **$-\frac{7}{2}$**

11. $1.9w + 7.9 = 0.9w - 3.8$  **−11.7**

12. $\frac{1}{7}x - x = -\frac{1}{7}(2x + 84)$  **21**

13. Find the complement of an angle whose measure is $62°$.  **28°**

14. Find the supplement of an angle whose measure is $74°$.  **106°**

**Solve for d.**

15. $d + 17y = 21$  **$d = 21 - 17y$**

16. $d(7 - x) = 4v$  **$d = \frac{4v}{7 - x}, x \neq 7$**

17. $7w + 3d = -12$

$$d = \frac{-12 - 7w}{3}$$

**The list below gives the prices of the same pair of sneakers at different stores. Use this set of data to complete Exercises 18–20.**

$$72, 63, 65, 72, 75, 70, 68, 72, 68$$

18. Find the mean of the sneaker prices.  **$69.44**

19. Find the median of the sneaker prices.  **$70**

20. Find the mode of the sneaker prices.  **$72**

# Ratios and Proportions

In mathematics, a **ratio** compares two numbers by division. A ratio that compares a number $x$ to a number $y$ can be written in the following ways.

$$x \text{ to } y \qquad x{:}y \qquad \frac{x}{y}$$

When a ratio compares two quantities with different units of measure, that ratio is called a **rate**. For example, a 7°F rise in temperature per hour is a rate and can be expressed as $\frac{7 \text{ degrees}}{1 \text{ hour}}$, or 7 degrees per hour.

Proportions are often used to solve problems involving ratios. You can use the means-extremes property of proportions to solve equations that have the form of a proportion.

| **Definition of Proportion** | An equation of the form $\frac{a}{b} = \frac{c}{d}$ stating that two ratios are equal is called a proportion. |
|---|---|
| **Means-Extremes Property of Proportions** | In a proportion, the product of the extremes is equal to the product of the means. If $\frac{a}{b} = \frac{c}{d}$, then $ad = bc$. |

**Example**  Solve $\frac{r}{8} = \frac{14}{3}$.

$$\frac{r}{8} = \frac{14}{3}$$

$$3r = 112$$

$$r = 37\frac{1}{3} \quad \text{The solution is } 37\frac{1}{3}.$$

## EXERCISES

**Solve each proportion.**

1. $\frac{w-1}{9} = \frac{7}{9}$  **8**

2. $\frac{3}{11} = \frac{9}{z}$  **33**

3. $\frac{a}{7} = \frac{15}{35}$  **3**

4. $\frac{0.25}{4} = \frac{0.3}{y}$  **4.8**

5. $\frac{4}{x+2} = \frac{16}{28}$  **5**

6. $\frac{9-2t}{7+t} = \frac{15}{27}$  **2**

7. $\frac{2b}{13} = \frac{8}{20}$  **$\frac{13}{5}$**

8. $\frac{m+3}{-5} = \frac{20-m}{-4}$  **$\frac{88}{9}$**

**Use a proportion to solve each problem.**

9. To make a model of the Rio Grande River, Angelica used 1 inch of clay for 50 miles of the actual river's length. Her model river was 38 inches long. How long is the Rio Grande?   **1900 miles**

10. $2\frac{1}{2}$ hours

10. Jorge finished 28 math problems in one hour. At that rate, how many hours will it take him to complete 70 math problems?

# Integration: Geometry
# Similar Triangles

Triangle *FGH* is similar to triangle *JKL*. The angles of the two triangles are congruent. They are called **corresponding angles**. The sides opposite corresponding angles are called **corresponding sides**. Proportions can be used to find the missing measures of similar triangles.

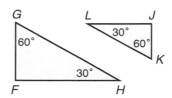

| **Similar Triangles** | If two triangles are similar, the measures of their corresponding sides are proportional, and the measures of their corresponding angles are equal. |
|---|---|

**Example**

Find the height of the apartment building.

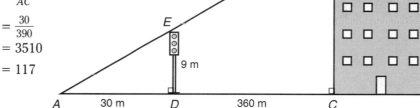

$\triangle ABC$ is similar to $\triangle AED$.

$$\frac{ED}{BC} = \frac{AD}{AC}$$

$$\frac{9}{x} = \frac{30}{390}$$

$$30x = 3510$$

$$x = 117$$

The apartment building is 117 meters high.

## EXERCISES

**Refer to the triangles below to answer the questions.**

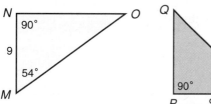

1. Which triangles are similar? **△MNO and △TUS**

**2. ∠M and ∠T; ∠N and ∠U; ∠O and ∠S**

2. Name the corresponding angles of the similar triangles.

3. Name the corresponding sides of the similar triangles.
   **MN and TU; MO and TS; NO and US**

4. **Surveying** At a certain time of the day, the Empire State Building casts a shadow 140 feet long. At the same time of day, a post 10 feet tall casts a shadow 1.12 feet long. How tall is the Empire State Building? **1250 feet**

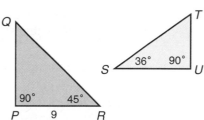

# Integration: Trigonometry
## Trigonometric Ratios

For right triangles, **trigonometric ratios** can be defined.

For $\angle A$:

$\overline{BC}$ is *opposite* $\angle A$.

$\overline{AC}$ is *adjacent* to $\angle A$.

$\overline{AB}$ is the *hypotenuse* and is opposite the right angle $C$.

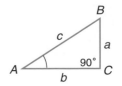

| Definition of Trigonometric Ratios | |
|---|---|
| sine of $\angle A = \dfrac{\text{measure of leg opposite } \angle A}{\text{measure of hypotenuse}}$ | $\sin A = \dfrac{a}{c}$ |
| cosine of $\angle A = \dfrac{\text{measure of leg adjacent to } \angle A}{\text{measure of hypotenuse}}$ | $\cos A = \dfrac{b}{c}$ |
| tangent of $\angle A = \dfrac{\text{measure of leg opposite } \angle A}{\text{measure of leg adjacent to } \angle A}$ | $\tan A = \dfrac{a}{b}$ |

**Example**

a. **Find cos B to the nearest thousandth.**

$\cos B = \dfrac{a}{c} = \dfrac{6}{14}$ or 0.429

b. **Use a scientific calculator to find the measure of $\angle B$.**

Enter: .429 $\boxed{\text{INV}}$ $\boxed{\text{COS}}$ *64.59588564*

The measure of $\angle B$ to the nearest degree is 65°.

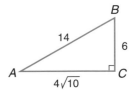

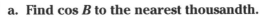

## EXERCISES

1. $A$: 0.441, 0.897, 0.492;
$B$: 0.897, 0.441, 2.033

1. Find the sine, cosine, and tangent of each acute angle. Round your answers to the nearest thousandth.

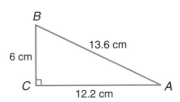

**Find each value to the nearest ten thousandth.**

2. sin 32°     3. cos 80°     4. tan 20°     5. sin 58°     6. cos 70°
   **0.5299**      **0.1736**      **0.3640**      **0.8480**      **0.3420**

**Use a calculator to find the measure of each angle to the nearest degree.**

7. sin $Q$ = 0.4695  **28°**   8. tan $D$ = 0.7002  **35°**   9. cos $G$ = 0.500  **60°**

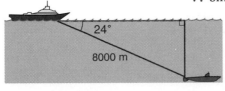

10. **Military**   A navy ship has located a submarine using sonar. The sonar reading shows that the distance to the submarine is 8000 meters and the angle of depression to the submarine is 24°. What is the depth of the submarine to the nearest meter?  **3254 meters**

# Percents

A percent problem may be easier to solve if a proportion is used.

| Percent Proportion |
| --- |
| $\dfrac{\text{percentage}}{\text{base}} = \text{rate}$ |
| or |
| $\dfrac{\text{percentage}}{\text{base}} = \dfrac{r}{100}$ |

**Example**

**a. 48 is what percent of 60?**

$\begin{array}{l}\text{percentage} \rightarrow \\ \text{base} \rightarrow\end{array} \dfrac{48}{60} = \dfrac{r}{100} \leftarrow rate$

$4800 = 60r$

$80 = r$

48 is 80% of 60.

**b. What number is 30% of 180?**

$\begin{array}{l}\text{percentage} \rightarrow \\ \text{base} \rightarrow\end{array} \dfrac{n}{180} = \dfrac{30}{100} \leftarrow rate$

$n = \dfrac{30}{100}(180)$

$n = 54$

54 is 30% of 180.

## EXERCISES

**Use a proportion to answer each question.**

1. 56.25%

2. $33\frac{1}{3}$%

5. 125

1. Forty-five is what percent of 80?
2. Twenty is what percent of 60?
3. What is 40% of 90?  **36**
4. Find 36% of 240.  **86.4**
5. Fifty-five is 44% of what number?
6. 8.4 is 12% of what number?  **70**

7. On Wednesday, Eric's Machine Shop received a shipment of 24 drill bits. Eric had ordered 40 drill bits. What percent of his order arrived on Wednesday?  **60%**

8. Mackenzie received a commission of 6% on the sale of a house. If the amount of her commission was $8400, what was the selling price of the house?  **$140,000**

9. According to the book *Are You Normal*, 33% of Americans are afraid of snakes, 8% are afraid of thunder and lightning, 4% by crowds and dogs, 2% of cats, 3% of driving a car or leaving the house, and $\frac{1}{3}$ are afraid of flying.  **a. 338 people**
   a. In a group of 1025 people, about how many are afraid of snakes?
   b. About how many are afraid of crowds?  **41 people**
   c. About how many are afraid of flying?  **342 people**

10. In 1995, 351 million pairs of athletic shoes were purchased. Women accounted for 42% of those sales, and men for about 33% of those sales. About how many pairs of athletic shoes were purchased by women and by men?  **W: about 147 million; M: about 116 million**

# Percent of Change

Some percent problems involve finding a percent of increase or decrease.

| Percent of Increase | Percent of Decrease |
|---|---|
| A basketball that cost $20 last year costs $22 this year. The price increased by $2 since last year. | A jacket that originally cost $80 is now on sale for $60. |
| $\frac{\text{amount of increase} \rightarrow}{\text{original price} \rightarrow} \frac{2}{20} = \frac{r}{100}$ | $\frac{\text{amount of decrease} \rightarrow}{\text{original price} \rightarrow} \frac{20}{80} = \frac{r}{100}$ |
| $200 = 20r$ | $2000 = 80r$ |
| $10 = r \text{ or } r = 10$ | $25 = r \text{ or } r = 25$ |
| The percent of increase is 10%. | The percent of decrease is 25%. |

The sales tax on a purchase is a percent of the purchase price. To find the total price, you must calculate the amount of sales tax and add it to the purchase price.

## EXERCISES

**Find the final price of each item. When there is a discount and sales tax, compute the discount first.**

1. compact disc: $12.00
   discount: 20%   **$9.60**

2. two concert tickets: $35.00
   student discount: 15%   **$29.75**

3. airline ticket: $348   **$243.60**
   early booking discount: 30%

4. photo calendar: $12.95
   sales tax: 6%   **$13.73**

5. class ring: $110
   group discount: 12%   **$103.58**
   sales tax: 7%

6. multimedia software: $49.95
   discount: 25%
   sales tax: 5%   **$39.33**

**Solve each problem. Round to the nearest tenth of a percent.**

7. **Consumerism**  According to the U.S. Bureau of Economic Analysis, Americans spent $318.8 billion on recreation in 1992. In 1993, spending on recreation in the United States had grown to $339.9 billion. What was the percent of increase in spending on recreation from 1992 to 1993?  **6.6%**

8. **Agriculture**  According to the U.S. Department of Agriculture, the number of farms in the United States in 1984 was 2,334,000. By 1994, this number had fallen to 2,065,000 farms. Find the percent of decrease in the number of farms from 1984 to 1994.  **11.5%**

# Integration: Probability
## Probability and Odds

The **probability** of an event is a ratio that tells how likely it is that the event will take place.

| Definition of Probabilty |
|---|
| $P(\text{event}) = \dfrac{\text{number of favorable outcomes}}{\text{number of possible outcomes}}$ |

**Example** ❶ **Ms. Michalski picks 8 of the 24 students in her class at random for a special project. What is the probability of being picked?**

$$P(\text{being picked}) = \frac{\text{number of students picked}}{\text{total number of students}}$$

The probability of being picked is $\frac{8}{24}$ or $\frac{1}{3}$.

The probability of any event has a value from 0 to 1. If the probability of an event is 0, it is impossible for the event to occur. An event that is certain to occur has a probability of 1. This can be expressed as $0 \le P(\text{event}) \le 1$.

The **odds** of an event occurring is the ratio of the number of ways an event can occur (successes) to the number of ways the event cannot occur (failures).

| Definition of Odds |
|---|
| $\text{Odds} = \dfrac{\text{number of sucessess}}{\text{number of failures}}$ |

**Example** ❷ **Find the odds that a member of Ms. Michalski's class will be picked for the special project.**

Number of successes: 8      Number of failures: 16

Odds of being picked = number of successes : number of failures

= 8:16 or 1:2

## EXERCISES

**Solve each problem.**

1. $\frac{1}{3}$

1. There are 3 brown puppies, 4 white puppies, and 5 spotted puppies in a pen. What is the probability of pulling out a white puppy at random?

2. $\frac{19}{31}$; 19:12

2. It will rain 5 times in March and snow 7 times. The other days it will be sunny. What is the probability of sun? What are the odds of sun?

**There are 300 freshmen, 250 sophomores, 200 juniors, and 250 seniors at a high school. Solve each problem.**

3. $\frac{3}{10}$

3. If one student is chosen at random, what is the probability that a freshman will be chosen?

4. What would be the odds of choosing a sophomore if all of the seniors were eliminated?   **1:2**

5. What are the odds that a junior will not be chosen?   **4:1**

6. What are the odds of choosing a senior at random?   **1:3**

# Weighted Averages

You can use charts to solve mixture problems.

**Example**  Ho Lee invested a portion of $24,000 at 6% interest and the balance at 8% interest. How much did he invest at each rate if his total income from both investments was $1720 after one year?

| Amount Invested | Rate | Annual Income |
|---|---|---|
| $x$ | 0.06 | 0.06$x$ |
| 24,000 − $x$ | 0.08 | 0.08(24,000 − $x$) |

$$\underset{\substack{\text{income from} \\ \text{6\% investment}}}{} + \underset{\substack{\text{income from} \\ \text{8\% investment}}}{} = \underset{\substack{\text{total} \\ \text{income}}}{}$$

$$0.06x + 0.08(24{,}000 - x) = 1720$$
$$0.06x + 1920 - 0.08x = 1720$$
$$-0.02x = -200$$
$$x = 10{,}000 \text{ and } 24{,}000 - x = 14{,}000$$

Mr. Lee invested $10,000 at 6% and $14,000 at 8%.

When an object moves without changing its speed, it is said to be in **uniform motion**. The formula $d = rt$ is used to solve uniform motion problems.

**Example**  Connie Cellucci left home driving at a speed of 62 miles per hour. How many hours did it take her to reach her destination 217 miles away?

$$d = rt$$
$$217 = 62t$$
$$3\frac{1}{2} = t \qquad \text{It will take Ms. Cellucci } 3\frac{1}{2} \text{ hours to drive 217 miles.}$$

# EXERCISES

1. How many grams of salt must be added to 90 grams of a 40% solution to obtain a 60% solution?   **45 grams**

2. $1\frac{3}{17}$ hours

2. Ms. Sessa and Mr. Schroeder each drove home from a business meeting. Mr. Schroeder traveled north at 80 kilometers per hour and Ms. Sessa traveled south at 90 kilometers per hour. In how many hours were they 200 kilometers apart?

3. Coffee Heaven sells Basic Decaf coffee for $6 per pound and French Vanilla coffee for $9 per pound. How many pounds of Basic Decaf coffee must be added to 20 pounds of French Vanilla coffee to make a mixture that sells for $7 per pound?   **40 pounds**

4. Alfredo left home at 7:00 A.M., riding his bike at 5 miles per hour. His sister Anel left 1 hour later, riding her bike at 6 miles per hour. At what time will Anel catch up to Alfredo if Anel is delayed 30 minutes by a flat tire?   **4 P.M.**

# Direct and Inverse Variation

If two variables $x$ and $y$ are related by the equation $y = kx$, where $k$ is a nonzero constant, then the equation is called a **direct variation**, and $k$ is called the **constant of variation**. If two variables $x$ and $y$ are related by the equation $xy = k$, where $k \neq 0$, then the equation is called an **inverse variation**.

**Example**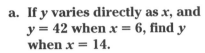

a. **If $y$ varies directly as $x$, and $y = 42$ when $x = 6$, find $y$ when $x = 14$.**

$$y = kx$$
$$42 = 6k$$
$$\frac{42}{6} = \frac{6k}{6}$$
$$7 = k$$

$$y = kx$$
$$y = 7(14)$$
$$y = 98$$

b. **If $y$ varies inversely as $x$, and $y = 8$ when $x = 9$, find $x$ when $y = 24$.**

$$xy = k$$
$$9(8) = k$$
$$72 = k$$

$$xy = k$$
$$24x = 72$$
$$\frac{24x}{24} = \frac{72}{24}$$
$$x = 3$$

## EXERCISES

**Solve. Assume that $y$ varies directly as $x$.**

1. If $y = 15$ when $x = 3$, find $y$ when $x = 8$. **40**

2. If $y = -49$ when $x = 7$, find $x$ when $y = 91$. **−13**

3. If $y = \frac{3}{8}$ when $x = 2$, find $y$ when $x = \frac{1}{4}$. **$\frac{3}{64}$**

4. If $y = \frac{4}{5}$ when $x = -\frac{3}{4}$, find $x$ when $y = -\frac{7}{10}$. **$\frac{21}{32}$**

**Solve. Assume that $y$ varies inversely as $x$.**

5. If $y = 10$ when $x = 7.5$, find $y$ when $x = 3$. **25**

6. If $y = -6$ when $x = 14$, find $y$ when $x = -5$. **$\frac{84}{5}$**

7. If $y = 18.1$ when $x = 12.4$, find $y$ when $x = 20$. **$\frac{5611}{500}$**

8. If $y = \frac{3}{8}$ and $x = \frac{1}{9}$, find $y$ when $x = \frac{1}{6}$. **$\frac{1}{4}$**

9. **Space** The weight of an object on Mars varies directly as its weight on Earth. An unmanned probe that weighs 500 pounds on Earth weighs 190 pounds on Mars. In the future, NASA hopes to send a manned mission to Mars. How much will an astronaut with gear weighing 220 pounds on Earth weigh on Mars? **$83\frac{3}{5}$ pounds**

**Solve each proportion.**

1. $\frac{t-1}{7} = \frac{6}{7}$   **7**

2. $\frac{4}{19} = \frac{6}{z}$   **$28\frac{1}{2}$**

3. $\frac{5}{x+2} = \frac{25}{30}$   **4**

4. At a certain time of the day, the NationsBank Tower in Atlanta, Georgia, casts a shadow 310 feet long. At the same time of day, a post 8 feet tall casts a shadow 2.42 feet long. How tall is the NationsBank Tower?   **1025 feet**

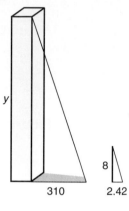

**Use the triangle at the right for Exercises 5 and 6.**

5. If $a = 9$ and $c = 16$, find the measure of $\angle A$ to the nearest degree.   **34°**

6. If $a = 12$, $b = 15$, and $c = 3\sqrt{41}$, find tan $B$.   **$\frac{5}{4}$**

7. 54.6 is what percent of 130?   **42%**

8. What number is 72% of 600?   **432**

9. In a survey, 29% of the respondents reported that they have returned rented videotapes to the store late. If 3200 people responded to the survey, how many have returned videotapes late?   **928**

10. The regular cost of a paperback book is $6.95. A discount store sells all of its paperbacks at a 25% discount. What is the cost of the paperback at the discount store?   **$5.21**

11. The price of an oil change increased from $19.95 to $22.94. What was the percent of increase?   **15%**

12. According to the NCAA, the annual number of Division I basketball games played was at an all-time high in 1992 at 8803 games. In 1995, only 8662 games were played. Find the percent of decrease in the number of Division I basketball games played from 1992 to 1995. Round to the nearest tenth of a percent.   **1.6%**

13. If the probability in favor of an event is $\frac{8}{15}$, what are the odds of that event occurring?   **8:7**

14. A box of sports cards contains 9 baseball cards, 7 football cards, and 4 basketball cards. What is the probability that a football card is chosen at random?   **$\frac{7}{20}$**

15. A factory has an order for 3000 bricks of cheese. Machine A can process 120 bricks of cheese per hour while Machine B can process 110 bricks of cheese per hour. Machine A starts at 9:00 A.M. and Machine B starts at 11:00 A.M. At what time will the two machines complete the job?   **11 P.M.**

16. A chemist has 40 liters of 20% saline solution. How many liters of 40% saline solution must be added to produce a 35% saline solution?   **120 liters**

17. If $y$ varies directly as $x$ and $y = 12$ when $x = 14$, find $y$ when $x = 50$.   **$42\frac{6}{7}$**

18. If $y$ varies inversely as $x$ and $y = 3$ when $x = 60$, find $y$ when $x = 100$.   **$1\frac{4}{5}$**

# The Coordinate Plane

In the diagram at the right, the two perpendicular lines, called the *x*-axis and the *y*-axis, divide the coordinate plane into Quadrants I, II, III, and IV. The point where the two axes intersect is called the **origin**. The origin is represented by the ordered pair $(0, 0)$.

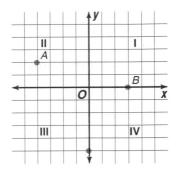

Every other point in the coordinate plane is also represented by an ordered pair of numbers. The ordered pair for point $A$ is $(-4, 2)$. We say that $-4$ is the *x*-coordinate of $A$ and 2 is the *y*-coordinate of $A$.

**Example**   **Write the ordered pair for the point $B$ on the diagram above.**

The *x*-coordinate is 3 and the *y*-coordinate is 0. Thus, the ordered pair is $(3, 0)$.

To graph any ordered pair $(x, y)$, begin at the origin. Move left or right $x$ units. From there, move up or down $y$ units. Draw a dot at that point.

## EXERCISES

**Graph each point on the same coordinate plane.**

1–6. See Teacher's Answer Key.

1. $C(-4, 0)$
2. $D(2, 2)$
3. $E(3, -5)$
4. $F(-2, 4)$
5. $G(-1, -3)$
6. $H(0, -3)$

**Write the ordered pair for each point shown at the right. Name the quadrant in which the point is located.**

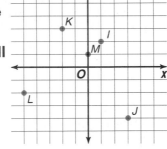

7. $I$ **(1, 2); I**
8. $J$ **(3, −4); IV**
9. $K$ **(−2, 3);II**
10. $L$ **(−5, −2); III**
11. $M$ **(0, 1); none**

12. **Computers**  Juan is a computer programmer. He is developing multimedia math software. Each screen in the program must be mapped out pixel by pixel. In the screen shown at the right, find the coordinates of each pixel making up the variable X.
**(3, 4), (3, 5), (3, 7), (3, 8), (4, 6), (5, 4), (5, 5), (5, 7), (5, 8)**

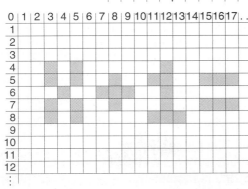

# Relations

A **relation** is a set of ordered pairs. The **domain** is the set of all first coordinates of the ordered pairs, and the **range** is the set of all second coordinates.

**Example**  State the domain and range of each relation.

a. $\{(7, 1), (7, 3), (7, 5)\}$    Domain = $\{7\}$; Range = $\{1, 3, 5\}$

b. $\{(2, 4), (3, 6), (4, 4)\}$    Domain = $\{2, 3, 4\}$; Range = $\{4, 6\}$

Relations can be expressed as ordered pairs, tables, graphs, and mappings. The relation $\{(-3, 4), (0, 6), (2, -1)\}$ can be expressed in each of the following ways.

| Ordered Pairs | Table | Graph | Mapping |
|---|---|---|---|
| $(-3, 4)$ $(0, 6)$ $(2, -1)$ | | | |

| x | y |
|---|---|
| -3 | 4 |
| 0 | 6 |
| 2 | -1 |

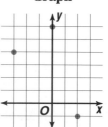

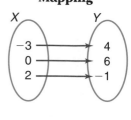

The **inverse** is obtained by switching the coordinates in each ordered pair.

## EXERCISES

**State the domain and range of each relation.**

1. $\{(5, 4), (-2, 5), (-3, 0), (4, 5), (5, 0)\}$   $D = \{-3, -2, 4, 5\}$; $R = \{0, 4, 5\}$

2. $\{(1.25, -0.3), (-14, 12), (6, 1.25)\}$   $D = \{-14, 1.25, 6\}$; $R = \{-0.3, 1.25, 12\}$

3. $\left\{\left(\frac{1}{3}, \frac{3}{8}\right), \left(-\frac{7}{9}, 4\right), \left(2\frac{1}{5}, -\frac{1}{4}\right)\right\}$   $D = \left\{-\frac{7}{9}, \frac{1}{3}, 2\frac{1}{5}\right\}$; $R = \left\{-\frac{1}{4}, \frac{3}{8}, 4\right\}$

**Express each relation shown as a set of ordered pairs. Then state the domain, range, and inverse of the relation.**

4.

| x | y |
|---|---|
| 3 | -1 |
| 5 | 4 |
| 7 | 2 |

**4–5. See Teacher's Answer Key.**

5.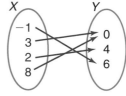

6. **Computers**  The table gives the percentage of public schools in the United States that have computers capable of using CD-ROM software.

| Percentage of Public Schools with CD-ROMs | | | | |
|---|---|---|---|---|
| Year | 1992 | 1993 | 1994 | 1995 |
| Percentage | 7 | 13 | 25 | 41 |

**Source:** Quality Education Data, Inc.

**6a. D = {1992, 1993, 1994, 1995}; R = {7, 13, 25, 41}**

**6c. The percentage of public schools with CD-ROMs is increasing.**

a. Determine the domain and range of the relation.

b. Graph the data.  **See Teacher's Answer Key.**

c. What conclusions might you make from the graph of the data?

# Equations as Relations

An equation in two variables describes a relation. It is often easier to determine the solution of such an equation by solving for one of the variables.

**Example**  Solve $4x - 5y = 4$ if the domain is $\{-4, -\frac{3}{2}, 6\}$.

First solve for $y$ in terms of $x$.

$4x - 5y = 4$

$\quad -5y = 4 - 4x$

$\quad\quad y = \dfrac{4 - 4x}{-5}$

Then substitute values of $x$.

| $x$ | $\dfrac{4 - 4x}{-5}$ | $y$ | $(x, y)$ |
|---|---|---|---|
| $-4$ | $\dfrac{4 - 4(-4)}{-5}$ | $-4$ | $(-4, -4)$ |
| $-\dfrac{3}{2}$ | $\dfrac{4 - 4\left(-\frac{3}{2}\right)}{-5}$ | $-2$ | $\left(-\dfrac{3}{2}, -2\right)$ |
| $6$ | $\dfrac{4 - 4(6)}{-5}$ | $4$ | $(6, 4)$ |

## EXERCISES

**Which ordered pairs are solutions of each equation?**

1. $a + 3b = 10$    **a.** $(3, 1)$    **b.** $(1, 3)$    **c.** $(10, 0)$    **d.** $(-2, 4)$    **b, c, d**

2. $5x + 2y = 18$    **a.** $(4, -1)$    **b.** $(3, 1)$    **c.** $(2, 4)$    **d.** $(1, 7)$    **a, c**

**Solve each equation if the domain is $\{-2, -1, 0, 1, 2\}$.**

3. $x - y = 3$    $\{(-2, -5), (-1, -4), (0, -3), (1, -2), (2, -1)\}$

4. $y = 2x + 6$    $\{(-2, 2), (-1, 4), (0, 6), (1, 8), (2, 10)\}$

5. $2x - 3y = 7$    $\left\{\left(-2, -3\frac{2}{3}\right), (-1, -3), \left(0, -2\frac{1}{3}\right), \left(1, -1\frac{2}{3}\right), (2, -1)\right\}$

6. $x + 4y = 12$    $\left\{\left(-2, 3\frac{1}{2}\right), \left(-1, 3\frac{1}{4}\right), (0, 3), \left(1, 2\frac{3}{4}\right), \left(2, 2\frac{1}{2}\right)\right\}$

7. $3x + 7y = 21$    $\left\{\left(-2, 3\frac{6}{7}\right), \left(-1, 3\frac{3}{7}\right), (0, 3), \left(1, 2\frac{4}{7}\right), \left(2, 2\frac{1}{7}\right)\right\}$

8. $2x - 9 = y$    $\{(-2, -13), (-1, -11), (0, -9), (1, -7), (2, -5)\}$

9. **Cooking** For mashed potatoes, some cooks recommend using one more potato than the number of people to be served.

   **a.** Write an equation describing the number of potatoes to use when making mashed potatoes. Let $x$ be the number of people to be served. Let $y$ be the number of potatoes to use.   $y = x + 1$

   **b.** Make a table of the solution set if the domain is $\{3, 4, 5, 6\}$

**9b.**

| $x$ | $y$ |
|---|---|
| 3 | 4 |
| 4 | 5 |
| 5 | 6 |
| 6 | 7 |

# Graphing Linear Equations

An equation whose graph is a straight line is called a **linear equation**.

> **Definition of Linear Equation**
>
> A **linear equation** is an equation that can be written in the form $Ax + By = C$, where $A$, $B$, and $C$ are any real numbers and $A$ and $B$ are not both zero.

**Drawing the Graph of a Linear Equation**

1. Solve the equation for one variable.
2. Set up a table of values for the variables.
3. Graph the ordered pairs and connect them with a line.

**Example**  **Draw the graph of $y + 2x = 2$.**

$$y + 2x = 2$$
$$y = 2 - 2x$$

| x | 2 − 2x | y | (x, y) |
|---|--------|---|--------|
| −1 | 2 − 2(−1) | 4 | (−1, 4) |
| 0 | 2 − 2(0) | 2 | (0, 2) |
| 1 | 2 − 2(1) | 0 | (1, 0) |

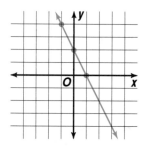

## EXERCISES

**Determine whether each equation is a linear equation. If an equation is linear, rewrite it in the form $Ax + By = C$.**

1. $5x = 3y + 6$
   **yes; $5x - 3y = 6$**

2. $x^2 + 14 = 2y$ **no**

3. $\frac{y}{9} = 3$ **yes; $y = 27$**

**Graph each equation.** **4–9. See Teacher's Answer Key.**

4. $x + 3y = 7$

5. $2s - t = 4$

6. $a + b = -3$

7. $-2x + 4y = 6$

8. $m - 2n = -2$

9. $\frac{3}{4}x - \frac{1}{4}y = 8$

10. **Employment** Maria Tomasso works as a sales representative. She receives a salary of $2200 per month plus a 4% commission on monthly sales. She estimates that her sales in October, November, and December will be $2000, $3500, and $2800.

    a. Graph ordered pairs that represent her incomes $y$ for the three monthly sales figures $x$. **See Teacher's Answer Key.**

    b. Will her total monthly income be more than $2300 in any of the three months? Explain.

**10b. Yes, for sales of $2800 and $3500 her income is greater than $2300.**

# Functions

A special type of relation is called a **function**.

| Definition of Function |
|---|
| A **function** is a relation in which each element of the domain is paired with *exactly* one element of the range. |

**Example**  **Is {(4, 2), (7, 1), (5, −1), (3, 2)} a function? Is the inverse a function?**

Since each element of the domain is paired with exactly one element of the range, the relation is a function. The inverse is not a function because 2 is paired with more than one element of the range.

The equation $y = 3x - 1$ can be written as $f(x) = 3x - 1$. If $x = 4$, then $f(4) = 3(4) - 1$, or 11. Thus, $f(4)$, which is read "$f$ of 4" is a way of referring to the value of $y$ that corresponds to $x = 4$.

**Example**  **If $f(x) = 5x + 4$, find $f(2)$ and $f(-1)$.**

$$f(2) = 5(2) + 4 \qquad\qquad f(-1) = 5(-1) + 4$$
$$= 10 + 4 \qquad\qquad\qquad = -5 + 4$$
$$= 14 \qquad\qquad\qquad\quad = -1$$

## EXERCISES

**Determine whether each relation is a function.**

1.  no    2. yes    3. no

4. yes
5. no
6. yes

4. {(2, 1), (4, 4), (3, 1)}     5. {(7, 3), (6, 4), (7, 5)}     6. {(2, 1), (−2, 1), (3, 1)}
7. $7x + 7 = 5y$  **yes**     8. $8 - y = 0$  **yes**     9. $y = x^2 + 7$  **yes**

**Given $f(x) = 6x + 4$ and $g(x) = x^2 + 2x - 1$, find each value.**

10. $f(2)$  **16**          11. $f(-3)$  **−14**          12. $g(0)$  **−1**
13. $g(2)$  **7**           14. $f(1)$  **10**            15. $g(-1)$  **−2**

16. **Business**  Viktor Alessandrovich owns a chain of ice cream parlors. He has noticed that his daily sales are dependent on the high temperature for the day. The formula for the relationship is $s = 2t^2 + 20t$, where $t$ represents the daily high temperature in degrees Fahrenheit and $s$ is the amount of daily sales.  **a. See Teacher's Answer Key.**

16b. As temperature increases, so do daily sales.

a. Suppose the domain for the function includes the set {60, 70, 75, 80, 85, 90}. Make a table using these values for $t$ and graph the function.

b. Describe the graph of the function. What trends do you see?

# Writing Equations from Patterns

You can find equations from relations. Suppose you purchased a number of packages of blank computer diskettes. If each package contained 10 diskettes, you could make a chart to show the relationship between the number of packages of diskettes and the total number of diskettes purchased. Use $a$ for the number of packages and $b$ for the number of diskettes.

| $a$ | 1 | 2 | 3 | 4 | 5 | 6 |
|---|---|---|---|---|---|---|
| $b$ | 10 | 20 | 30 | 40 | 50 | 60 |

This relationship can also be shown as an equation. Since $b$ is always 10 times $a$, the equation is $b = 10a$. Another way to discover this relationship is to study the difference between successive values of $a$ and $b$.

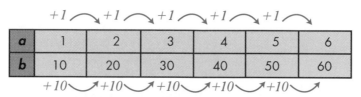

| $a$ | 1 | 2 | 3 | 4 | 5 | 6 |
|---|---|---|---|---|---|---|
| $b$ | 10 | 20 | 30 | 40 | 50 | 60 |

This suggests the relation $b = 10a$.

## EXERCISES

**Write an equation for each relation. Then complete each chart.**

1.

| $a$ | 0 | 1 | 2 | 3 | 4 | 5 |
|---|---|---|---|---|---|---|
| $b$ | 0 | $\frac{1}{4}$ | $\frac{1}{2}$ | $\frac{3}{4}$ | 1 | $\frac{5}{4}$ |

$b = \frac{1}{4}a$

2.

| $x$ | −2 | −1 | 0 | 1 | 2 | 3 |
|---|---|---|---|---|---|---|
| $y$ | 0 | 3 | 6 | 9 | 12 | 15 |

$y = 3x + 6$

3.

| $x$ | −1 | 0 | 1 | 2 | 3 | 4 |
|---|---|---|---|---|---|---|
| $y$ | 3 | 5 | 7 | 9 | 11 | 13 |

$y = 2x + 5$

4.

| $m$ | −3 | −2 | −1 | 0 | 1 | 2 |
|---|---|---|---|---|---|---|
| $n$ | 1 | 0 | −1 | −2 | −3 | −4 |

$n = -m - 2$

5. **Sales**  Kauffner's Sporting Goods, Inc., offers an annual bonus to the employees of its stores. The bonus is based on the amount of sales over the store's target sales level. The table below illustrates the relationship between sales and annual bonus.

| Sales over target level | $10,000 | $20,000 | $25,000 | $30,000 | $50,000 |
|---|---|---|---|---|---|
| Bonus | $200 | $400 | $500 | $600 | $1000 |

a. Write an equation in functional notation for the relation.  $f(x) = 0.02x$

b. Estimate the amount of an employee's annual bonus if the store's sales are $17,000 over the target level.  **$340**

# Integration: Statistics
# Measures of Variation

A *measure of variation* called the **range** describes the spread of numbers in a set of data. To find the range, determine the difference between the greatest and least values in the set.

*Quartiles* divide the data into four equal parts. The **upper quartile** divides the top half into two equal parts. The **lower quartile** divides the bottom half into two equal parts. Another measure of variation uses the upper and lower quartile values to determine the **interquartile range**. Study the data below.

lower quartile ⌐                    ⌐median = 62   ⌐upper quartile

4    14    20    33    40    51    73    79    90    90    94    95

The lower quartile is the median of the lower half (26.5). The upper quartile is the median of the upper half (90). The range is 95 − 4 = 91. The interquartile range is 90 − 26.5 = 63.5.

## EXERCISES

**Find the range, median, upper quartile, lower quartile, and interquartile range for each set of data.**

1. 29; 86.5; 90.5; 82; 8.5

2. 8; 7; 8; 6.5; 1.5

3. 16; 28; 34; 24.5; 9.5

4. 6; 15; 17.5; 13.5; 4

5. 10; 5; 6.5; 2.5; 4

6. 4.5; 12.5; 13.5; 10; 3.5

1. | Algebra Test Scores | | |
   |---|---|---|
   | 79 | 68 | 82 |
   | 86 | 82 | 91 |
   | 94 | 88 | 85 |
   | 97 | 87 | 90 |

2.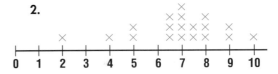

3. 20, 24, 36, 30, 28, 25, 35, 27, 33

4. 14, 19, 16, 13

5. 7, 2, 3, 5, 5, 10, 0, 6

6. 9.5, 12.5, 14, 13, 10.5,

7. | Stem | Leaf |
   |---|---|
   | 5 | 3 8 8 9 |
   | 6 | 1 2 2 2 4 6 |
   | 7 | 7 7 7 8 9 9 |

   *6 | 2 = 62*   **26; 63; 77; 60; 17**

8. | Stem | Leaf |
   |---|---|
   | 11 | 1 3 4 5 |
   | 12 | 2 2 4 4 |
   | 13 | 1 3 3 3 4 5 |

   *13 | 3 = 133*   **24; 124; 133; 115; 18**

9. The number of recreational visits to the most-visited sites in the U.S. National Park System in 1994 are given in the table at the right. Find the range, median, upper and lower quartiles, and interquartile range.
**12,000,000; 7,500,000; 12,500,000; 5,000,000; 7,500,000**

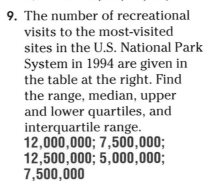

| National Park Site | Number of visits (millions) |
|---|---|
| Blue Ridge Parkway | 17 |
| Golden Gate Recreational Area | 15 |
| Lake Mead Recreational Area | 10 |
| Great Smoky Mountains | 9 |
| George Washington Parkway | 6 |
| National Capital Parks | 5 |
| Natchez Trace | 5 |
| Cape Cod Seashore | 5 |

**Source:** U.S. National Park Service

**Use the table to complete Exercises 1 and 2.**

| x | y |
|---|---|
| 3 | 12 |
| 0 | 5 |
| −4 | −8 |

1. Write the relation as a set of ordered pairs.
   {(3, 12), (0, 5), (−4, −8)}

2. State the domain, range, and inverse of the relation.
   2. D = {3, 0, −4}, R = {12, 5, −8}, I = {(12, 3), (5, 0), (−8, −4)}

3. Graph these points on the same coordinate plane. **See Teacher's Answer Key.**

   $P(3, 0)$      $Q(−2, 6)$      $R(4, −1)$      $S(0, 5)$

4. Name the quadrant in which each point is located.

   $A(−5, −7)$ **III**      $B(2, 2)$ **I**      $C(9, −13)$ **IV**

5. Draw a mapping for the relation {(0, 5), (6, 1), (3, 5), (4, −2)}.

   5. 
   
   X: 0, 3, 4, 6    Y: 2, 1, 5

6. Which ordered pairs are solutions of the equation $2x + 5y = −18$? **c**

   **a.** $(−3, −2)$      **b.** $(10, −1)$      **c.** $(−9, 0)$      **d.** $(12, −2)$

**Solve each equation if the domain is {−2, 0, 2, 4}.**

7. $x − 2y = 8$
   {(−2, −5), (0, −4), (2, −3), (4, −2)}

8. $y = 3x + 10$
   {(−2, 4), (0, 10), (2, 16), (4, 22)}

**Graph each equation. 9–11. See Teacher's Answer Key.**

9. $a − 2b = 9$      10. $3m + 2n = 5$      11. $x + y = −6$

12. Determine whether each relation is a function.

    **a.** {(3, 4), (5, 5), (6, 4)} **function**

    **b.** {(1, 0), (2, 0), (5, 0)} **function**

    **c.** {(1, 9), (−3, 6), (1, −1)} **not a function**

13. Given $f(x) = 7x + 12$, find $f(3)$. **33**

14. Given $g(x) = 2x^2 + 5$, find $g(2)$. **3**

**Write an equation for the relation in each chart.**

15.

| m | 0 | 1 | 2 | 3 | 4 | 5 |
|---|---|---|---|---|---|---|
| n | −2 | 1 | 4 | 7 | 10 | 13 |

$n = 3m − 2$

16.

| s | −2 | −1 | 0 | 1 | 2 |
|---|---|---|---|---|---|
| t | −19 | −7 | 5 | 17 | 29 |

$t = 12s + 5$

**The circulations of the top public libraries in the United States in 1994–1995 are listed in the table at the right.**

17. Find the range and median of the library circulation data. **8.1; 11.8**

18. Find the upper quartile, lower quartile, and interquartile range for the library circulation data. **12.95; 10.95; 2**

| Name of Public Library | Circulation (millions) |
|---|---|
| Los Angeles (CA) | 18.3 |
| Queens Borough (NY) | 13.6 |
| King County (Seattle, WA) | 12.3 |
| Los Angeles County (CA) | 11.9 |
| Cincinnati & Hamilton County (OH) | 11.7 |
| Baltimore County (MD) | 11.0 |
| Columbus (OH) | 10.9 |
| New York (NY) | 10.2 |

**Source:** Public Library Association

# Slope

The ratio of *rise* to *run* is called **slope**. The slope of a line describes its steepness, or rate of change.

| Definition of Slope |
| --- |
| The slope $m$ of a line is the ratio of the change in the $y$-coordinates to the corresponding change in the $x$-coordinates.<br><br>$$\text{Slope} = \frac{\text{change in } y}{\text{change in } x} \text{ or } m = \frac{\text{change in } y}{\text{change in } x}$$ |

On a coordinate plane, a line extending from lower left to upper right has a positive slope. A line extending from upper left to lower right has a negative slope. The slope of a horizontal line is zero. A vertical line has *no slope*.

The slope of a nonvertical line can be determined from the coordinates of any two points on the line.

| Determining Slope Given Two Points |
| --- |
| Given the coordinates of two points, $(x_1, y_1)$ and the $(x_2, y_2)$ on a line, the slope $m$ can be found as follows:<br><br>$$m = \frac{y_2 - y_1}{x_2 - x_1}, \text{ where } x_1 \neq x_2.$$ |

**Example**  Determine the slope of the line that passes through $(-3, 2)$ and $(6, -4)$.

$$m = \frac{y_2 - y_1}{x_2 - x_1}$$
$$= \frac{-4 - 2}{6 - (-3)}$$
$$= \frac{-6}{9} = -\frac{2}{3}$$

## EXERCISES

**Determine the slope of the line that passes through each pair of points.**

1. $(3, 7), (4, 5)$  **−2**
2. $(10, -2), (6, 3)$  $-\frac{5}{4}$
3. $(3, 0), (9, 1)$  $\frac{1}{6}$
4. $(0, 5), (8, -9)$  $-\frac{7}{4}$
5. $(-2, -2), (-1, 7)$  **9**
6. $(4, -3), (-9, 0)$  $-\frac{3}{13}$

**Determine the value of $r$ so the line that passes through each pair of points has the given slope.**

7. $(8, 6), (r, 2), m = \frac{4}{3}$  **5**
8. $(9, -7), (3, r), m = -1$  **−1**
9. $(2, r), (0, -6), m = \frac{3}{2}$  **−3**
10. $(r, 1), (6, -3), m = 2$  **8**
11. $(4, r), (-1, -5), m = \frac{8}{5}$  **3**
12. $(8, r), (r, 3), m = -\frac{1}{6}$  **2**

13. **Road Construction**  A portion of the John Scott Memorial Highway in Steubenville, Ohio, has a grade of 12%. The length of this portion is approximately 1.1 miles. What is the change in elevation from the top of the grade to the bottom of the grade in feet?  **697 feet**

# Writing Linear Equations in Point-Slope and Standard Forms

If you know the slope of a line and the coordinates of one point on the line, you can write an equation of the line by using the **point-slope form**. For a given point $(x_1, y_1)$ on a nonvertical line with slope $m$, the point-slope form of a linear equation is $y - y_1 = m(x - x_1)$.

| Standard Form |
|---|
| Any linear equation can be expressed in the form $Ax + By = C$, where $A$, $B$, and $C$ are integers, $A \geq 0$, and $A$ and $B$ are not both zero. This is called the **standard form**. |

**Example** **1**

a. Write the point-slope form of an equation of the line that passes through (3, 8) and has a slope of $-\frac{2}{7}$.

$$y - y_1 = m(x - x_1)$$
$$y - 8 = -\frac{2}{7}(x - 3)$$

b. Write $y - 6 = 4(x + 3)$ in standard form.

$$y - 6 = 4(x + 3)$$
$$y - 6 = 4x + 12$$
$$-4x + y = 18$$
$$4x - y = -18$$

You can also find an equation of a line if you know the coordinates of two points on the line. First, find the slope of the line. Then write an equation of the line by using the point-slope form or the standard form.

## EXERCISES

1. $7x - 10y = -25$
2. $3x - y = -3$
3. $3x + y = 13$
4. $8x + 9y = 44$
5. $x - 6y = 36$
6. $y - 5 = \frac{3}{10}(x - 7)$
7. $y - 5 = \frac{3}{10}(x - 7)$
8. $y - 4 = -\frac{2}{9}(x - 12)$
9. $y - 4 = 6(x - 4)$
10. $y + 2 = \frac{2}{13}(x - 4)$
11. $y - 6 = -1(x - 7)$
12. $y + 9 = -3(x + 4)$

**Write the standard form of an equation of the line that passes through the given point and has the given slope.**

1. $(5, 6)$, $m = \frac{7}{10}$
2. $(-1, 0)$, $m = 3$
3. $(7, -8)$, $m = -3$
4. $(1, 4)$, $m = -\frac{8}{9}$
5. $(6, -5)$, $m = \frac{1}{6}$
6. $(9, 6)$, $m = 0$  $y = 6$

**Write the point-slope form of an equation of the line that passes through each pair of points.**

7. $(7, 5)$, $(-3, 2)$
8. $(-6, 8)$, $(12, 4)$
9. $(4, 4)$, $(2, -8)$
10. $(-9, -4)$, $(4, -2)$
11. $(6, 7)$, $(7, 6)$
12. $(-4, -9)$, $(-6, -3)$

13. **Painting**   Vanessa is painting a wall mural. To paint the perspective correctly, she must connect two points on the wall with a line. One point is two feet from the bottom of the painting, three feet from the left side of the painting, and has coordinates (3, 2). The other point is seven feet from the bottom of the painting and ten feet from the left of the painting.

   a. Find an equation for the line connecting these points in point-slope form.   **13a.** $y - 2 = \frac{5}{7}(x - 3)$

   b. Vanessa has painted the line on her mural but is worried that the line isn't straight. The line she has painted goes through the point (6, 5). Has she painted the line correctly?   **no**

# Integration: Statistics
## Scatter Plots and Best-Fit Lines

A **scatter plot** is a graph that shows the relationship between paired data. The scatter plot may reveal a pattern, or association, between the paired data. This association can be negative or positive. The association is said to be positive when a line suggested by the points slants upward.

The scatter plot at the right represents the relationship between the amount of time Anita spends on her Spanish homework each week and her score on her weekly Spanish quiz. Since the points suggest a line that slants upward, there seems to be a positive relationship between the paired data. In general, the scatter plot seems to show that the more Anita studies, the better her quiz score.

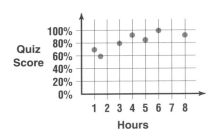

## EXERCISES

**Solve each problem.**

1. The table at the right shows the gasoline/mileage record for a certain car. At each gasoline fill-up, the car's owner recorded the amount of gasoline used since the previous fill-up and the distance traveled on that amount of gasoline.

   a. Draw a scatter plot from the data in the table.   **See Teacher's Answer Key.**

   **1b. gallons of gasoline and the miles traveled**

   b. What are the paired data?

   **1c. Yes, there is a strong positive correlation.**

   c. Is there a relationship between the gasoline used and the distance driven?

| Gasoline/Mileage Record ||
| Gallons of Gasoline | Miles Traveled |
| --- | --- |
| 9.8 | 250 |
| 7.9 | 200 |
| 9.1 | 240 |
| 8.0 | 210 |
| 7.5 | 185 |
| 9.3 | 255 |
| 9.5 | 250 |

2. Alex's biking speed after 10 minutes was 25 mi/h; at 30 minutes, 22 mi/h; at 45 minutes, 20 mi/h; and at 60 minutes, 19 mi/h.

   **2a. See Teacher's Answer Key.**

   a. Make a scatter plot pairing time biked with biking speed.

   b. How is the data related, positively, negatively, or not at all?   **negatively**

3. The table below shows the percent of children who are overweight ranked by the hours per day they spend watching television.

   **3a. See Teacher's Answer Key.**

   a. Draw a scatter plot for these data.

   b. Write an equation for the best-fit line.

   **3b. $y = 4.9x + 10.5$**

   c. What conclusion might you draw from these data?

   **3c. The more television a child watches, the greater the likelihood that he or she will be overweight.**

| Hours of TV Per Day | Percent Overweight |
| --- | --- |
| 1 | 12 |
| 2 | 23 |
| 3 | 28 |
| 4 | 30 |
| 5 or more | 33 |

# Writing Linear Equations in Slope-Intercept Form

The $x$-coordinate of the point where a line crosses the $x$-axis is called the **$x$-intercept**. Similarly, the $y$-coordinate of the point where the line crosses the $y$-axis is called the **$y$-intercept**.

| Slope-Intercept Form of a Linear Equation |
|---|
| Given the slope $m$ and the $y$-intercept $b$ of a line, the slope-intercept form of an equation of the line is $y = mx + b$. |

If an equation is given in standard form $Ax + By = C$ and $B$ is not zero, the slope of the line is $-\frac{A}{B}$ and the $y$-intercept is $\frac{C}{B}$. The $x$-intercept is $\frac{C}{A}$, where $A \neq 0$.

**Example**

Find the $x$- and $y$-intercepts of the graph of $2x - 6y = -12$. Then write the equation in slope-intercept form.

Since $A = 2$, $B = -6$, and $C = -12$,

$$\frac{C}{A} = \frac{-12}{2} \qquad \frac{C}{B} = \frac{-12}{-6} \qquad m = -\frac{A}{B}$$

$$= -6 \qquad\qquad = 2 \qquad\qquad = \frac{1}{3}$$

Thus, the $x$-intercept is $-6$, and the $y$-intercept is 2. The equation of the line in slope-intercept form is $y = \frac{1}{3}x + 2$.

## EXERCISES

**Find the $x$- and $y$-intercepts of the graph of each equation.**

1. $4x + 8y = 16$  **4; 2**

2. $2x - 7y = -4$  $-2; \frac{4}{7}$

3. $4x - 2y = 9$  $\frac{9}{4}; -\frac{9}{2}$

4. $3x + 6y = -13$  $-\frac{13}{3}; -\frac{13}{6}$

**Write an equation in slope-intercept form of a line with the given slope and $y$-intercept. Then write the equation in standard form.**

5. $m = 0$, $b = 5$  $y = 5$; $y = 5$

6. $m = 3$, $b = 1$

7. $m = -9$, $b = 8$

8. $m = 2$, $b = -7$

6. $y = 3x + 1$; $3x - y = -1$

7. $y = -9x + 8$; $9x + y = 8$

8. $y = 2x - 7$; $2x - y = 7$

9. $-\frac{1}{7}; \frac{22}{7}; y = -\frac{1}{7}x + \frac{22}{7}$

12. $\frac{35}{2}; -19; y = \frac{35}{2}x - 19$

**Find the slope and $y$-intercept of the graph of each equation. Then write each equation in slope-intercept form.**

9. $0.1x + 0.7y = 2.2$

10. $5x + 8y = 9$  $-\frac{5}{8}; \frac{9}{8}; y = -\frac{5}{8}x + \frac{9}{8}$

11. $4x - y = 4$  **4; −4; $y = 4x - 4$**

12. $35x - 2y = 38$

13. **Computers** A popular on-line service offers a light-usage payment plan. With this plan, customers pay a $4.95 monthly charge, which includes three hours of use. Customers are charged $2.50 per hour for each additional hour of use beyond the first three hours.

   a. Write an equation to represent the line that shows the total monthly amount charged by the on-line service for a customer who spends more than three hours on-line per month.  $y = 2.50x + 4.95$

13b. **Switch to the unlimited usage plan.**

   b. Suppose you spend an additional 7 hours on-line. Use the equation from part a to determine whether you should switch to the on-line service's unlimited usage plan for $19.95 per month.

# Graphing Linear Equations

There are three methods you can use for graphing equations. You can find two ordered pairs that satisfy the equation, the $x$- and $y$-intercepts, or the slope and $y$-intercept.

**Example** **1** **Graph $2x - 3y = 12$ by using the $x$- and $y$-intercepts.**

The equation is in standard form $Ax + By = C$.

The $x$-intercept is $\frac{C}{A}$, or 6.

The $y$-intercept is $\frac{C}{B}$, or $-4$.

Thus, the graph contains the points $(6, 0)$ and $(0, -4)$.

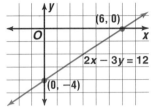

**Example** **2** **Graph $y = \frac{3}{4}x + 3$ by using the slope and $y$-intercept.**

The $y$-intercept is 3, and the slope is $\frac{3}{4}$.

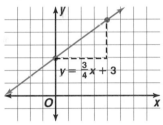

## EXERCISES

1–4. See Teacher's Answer Key.

**Graph each equation by using the $x$- and $y$-intercepts.**

1. $3x - 5y = 15$

2. $x + 7y = 14$

**Graph each equation by using the slope and $y$-intercept.**

3. $y = \frac{1}{5}x + 2$

4. $y = \frac{3}{4}x - 3$

5. **Biology** As the temperature increases, the number of times a cricket chirps per minute also increases. The temperature can be approximated by the equation $T = \frac{1}{4}c + 40$, where $c$ represents the number of cricket chirps per minute and $T$ is the temperature in degrees Fahrenheit.

   a. Graph the equation. **See Teacher's Answer Key.**

   b. On a summer evening you hear a cricket chirping outside your window. Suppose the cricket chirps 132 times per minute. What is the temperature outside? **73°**

# Integration: Geometry
# Parallel and Perpendicular Lines

When you graph two lines, you may encounter the two special types of graphs described at the right.

| Parallel Lines and Perpendicular Lines |
| --- |
| If two nonvertical lines have the same slope, then they are **parallel**. All vertical lines are parallel. |
| If the product of the slopes of two lines is $-1$, then the lines are **perpendicular**. In a plane, vertical lines and horizontal lines are perpendicular. |

**Example**

Write an equation in slope-intercept form of the line that passes through $(3, 0)$ and is parallel to the graph of $5x - 3y = 1$.

The slope of the graph is $-\dfrac{A}{B} = -\dfrac{5}{-3} = \dfrac{5}{3}$.

The slope-intercept form of an equation whose graph is parallel to the original graph is $y = \dfrac{5}{3}x + b$. Substitute $(3, 0)$ into the equation and solve for $b$.

$0 = \dfrac{5}{3}(3) + b$

$b = -5$   The $y$-intercept is $-5$.

The equation of the line is $y = \dfrac{5}{3}x - 5$.

Since $\dfrac{5}{3} \cdot \left(-\dfrac{3}{5}\right) = -1$, any line that is perpendicular to the line in the example has an equation of the form $y = -\dfrac{3}{5}x + b$. If the line includes the point $(5, 7)$, then $7 = -\dfrac{3}{5}(5) + b$ and thus, $b = 10$. The equation of the line is $y = -\dfrac{3}{5}x + 10$.

# EXERCISES

**Write an equation in slope-intercept form of the line that passes through the given point and is parallel to the graph of each equation.**

**1.** $y = 4x - 5$; $(1, 6)$
$y = 4x + 2$

**2.** $y = -\dfrac{1}{3}x + 7$; $(8, 0)$
$y = -\dfrac{1}{3}x + \dfrac{8}{3}$

**3.** $4x - 9y = 18$, $(-3, 2)$
$y = \dfrac{4}{9}x + \dfrac{10}{3}$

**Write an equation in slope-intercept form of the line that passes through the given point and is perpendicular to the graph of each equation.**

**4.** $x - 2y = 5$; $(1, 4)$
$y = -2x + 6$

**5.** $y = 5x + 12$; $(-6, 2)$
$y = -\dfrac{1}{5}x + \dfrac{4}{5}$

**6.** $4x + y = 0$; $(3, -3)$
$y = \dfrac{1}{4}x - \dfrac{15}{4}$

**7. Transportation**   In an aerial photograph, one rail in a set of railroad tracks has the equation $y = 0.73x + 3.6$. Find the equation of the other rail.   $y = 0.73x + 8.3$

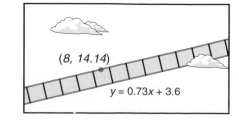
(8, 14.14)

$y = 0.73x + 3.6$

# Integration: Geometry
# Midpoint of a Line Segment

The **midpoint** of a line segment is the point that is halfway between the endpoints of the line segment.

| Midpoint of a Line Segment |
| --- |
| The coordinates of the midpoint of a line segment whose endpoints are at $(x_1, y_1)$ and $(x_2, y_2)$ are given by $\left( \frac{x_1 + x_2}{2}, \frac{y_1 + y_2}{2} \right)$. |

**Example** ● Find the coordinates of the midpoint of a segment whose endpoints are $A(-2, 3)$ and $B(8, 5)$.

$$(x, y) = \left( \frac{x_1 + x_2}{2}, \frac{y_1 + y_2}{2} \right)$$

$$= \left( \frac{-2 + 8}{2}, \frac{3 + 5}{2} \right)$$

$$= (3, 4)$$

The coordinates of the midpoint of $\overline{AB}$ are $(3, 4)$.

## EXERCISES

**Find the coordinates of the midpoint of a segment with each pair of endpoints.**

3. $\left( \frac{9}{2}, 0 \right)$

5. $\left( 4, -\frac{7}{2} \right)$

6. $\left( \frac{3}{2}, \frac{3}{2} \right)$

8. $\left( 32, \frac{79}{2} \right)$

9. $(3a, 3b)$

1. $E(7, 4), F(3, 2)$  **(5, 3)**  2. $K(1, 2), L(7, 3)$  $\left( 4, \frac{5}{2} \right)$  3. $A(0, -7), B(9, 7)$

4. $P\left( 1, \frac{1}{3} \right), Q\left( 3, \frac{1}{6} \right)$  $\left( 2, \frac{1}{4} \right)$  5. $I(5, -5), J(3, -2)$    6. $S(2, 8), T(1, -5)$

7. $G(3, 7), H(9, 9)$  **(6, 8)**  8. $M(64, 69), N(0, 10)$    9. $C(2a, 3b), D(4a, 3b)$

**If P is the midpoint of the segment MN, find the coordinates of the missing point.**

10. $M(7, 3), N(5, 4)$  $P\left( 6, \frac{7}{2} \right)$    11. $N(-9, 39), P(-1, 4)$  **M(7, −31)**

12. $N(-9, -2), P(-4, 0)$  **M(1, 2)**    13. $M(31, 50), P(40, 23)$  **N(49, −4)**

14. $M(10, -9), N(22, -15)$  **P(16, −12)** 15. $N(9, 3), P(-6, -2)$  **M(−21, −7)**

16. **Employment**  According to the U.S. Department of Labor, the average earnings of production workers in 1990 was $10.01 per hour. In 1994 the average earnings of production workers was $11.13 per hour.
 a. Use the data to form two ordered pairs.  **(1990, 10.01), (1994, 11.13)**
 b. Graph the ordered pairs.  **See Teacher's Answer Key.**
 c. Find the midpoint of the line segment joining the two pairs.  **(1992, 10.57)**
 d. What does this midpoint tell you?

**16d. In 1992, the average earnings of production workers was $10.57 per hour.**

# CHAPTER 6 TEST

**Determine the slope of the line that passes through each pair of points.**

1. $(6, 9), (1, 10)$   $-\dfrac{1}{5}$

2. $(8, -3), (2, 5)$   $-\dfrac{4}{3}$

3. Determine the value of $r$ so the line that passes through $(10, r)$ and $(8, 15)$ has a slope of $-\dfrac{7}{2}$.   **8**

**Write the standard form of an equation of the line satisfying the given conditions.**

4. passes through $(1, 3)$ and has a slope of $\dfrac{5}{8}$   $5x - 8y = -19$

5. passes through $(12, 3)$ and has a slope of $0$   $y = 3$

6. passes through $(4, 7)$ and $(-3, 2)$   $5x - 7y = -29$

**The value of U.S. exports and imports (in billions of dollars) for selected years from 1970 to 1994 are listed in the table at the right. Use the data for Exercises 7 and 8.**   **7. See Teacher's Answer Key.**

| Year | Exports | Imports |
|------|---------|---------|
| 1970 | 43 | 40 |
| 1975 | 108 | 99 |
| 1980 | 221 | 245 |
| 1985 | 213 | 345 |
| 1990 | 394 | 495 |
| 1991 | 422 | 485 |
| 1992 | 448 | 533 |
| 1993 | 465 | 581 |
| 1994 | 513 | 663 |

7. Make a scatter plot of the data with the value of exports on the horizontal axis and the value of imports on the vertical axis.

8. Does the data have *positive, negative,* or *no* correlation?   **positive**

9. Find the $x$- and $y$-intercepts of the graph of $9x - 3y = 5$.   $\dfrac{5}{9}; -\dfrac{5}{3}$

10. Write an equation in slope-intercept form of a line that has a slope of $-4$ and $y$-intercept of $7$.   $y = -4x + 7$

11. Find the slope and $y$-intercept of the graph of $0.3x + 1.4y = 4$.   $-\dfrac{3}{14}; \dfrac{20}{7}$

12. Graph $4x - y = 16$ by using the $x$- and $y$-intercepts.   **See Teacher's Answer Key.**

13. Graph $y = \dfrac{3}{5}x - 4$ by using the slope and $y$-intercept.   **See Teacher's Answer Key.**

14. Write an equation in slope-intercept form of the line that passes through $(-3, -5)$ and is parallel to the graph $y = -\dfrac{3}{4}x + 6$.   $y = -\dfrac{3}{4}x - \dfrac{29}{4}$

**Write an equation in slope-intercept form of the line that passes through the given point and is perpendicular to the graph of each equation.**

15. $5x - y = 5; (0, 9)$   $y = -\dfrac{1}{5}x + 9$

16. $y = 3x + 17; (-7, 4)$   $y = -\dfrac{1}{3}x + \dfrac{5}{3}$

**Find the coordinates of the midpoint of a segment with each pair of endpoints.**

17. $A(3, -12), B(7, 9)$   $\left(5, -\dfrac{3}{2}\right)$

18. $I(13, -4), J(7, -6)$   $(10, -5)$

19. If $P$ is the midpoint of the segment $MN$, find the coordinates of the missing point.
$N(-7, -3), P(-14, 6)$   $M(-21, 15)$

1. Write the expression $7 \cdot a \cdot a \cdot b \cdot c \cdot c$ using exponents.  **C**

   A. $7a^2c^2$

   B. $7^2a^2bc^2$

   C. $7a^2bc^2$

   D. $7a^3bc^2$

2. Name the property illustrated by $3p(p + 3) = 3p^2 + 9p$.  **C**

   A. associative property of addition

   B. associative property of multiplication

   C. distributive property

   D. commutative property of multiplication

3. Evaluate $2x^2y^2 - 4xy$ if $x = 2$ and $y = 5$.  **A**

   A. 160

   B. $-20$

   C. 40

   D. 30

4. Simplify $\frac{6 \cdot 7 + 3}{3^2} - \frac{50 - 5^2}{5}$.  **C**

   A. $-400$

   B. $\frac{5}{3}$

   C. 0

   D. 5

5. Simplify $5x^2 - 9x + 18 - 2x^2 + 6x + 12$.  **D**

   A. $7x^2 + 3x - 30$

   B. $-7x^2 - 3x + 30$

   C. $3x^2 + 3x - 30$

   D. $3x^2 - 3x + 30$

6. Simplify $-1\frac{1}{2} + \frac{2}{3} - \frac{3}{4}$.  **B**

   A. $-\frac{2}{13}$

   B. $-\frac{19}{12}$

   C. $-\frac{5}{12}$

   D. $\frac{7}{24}$

7. Simplify $\frac{64m + 88n}{-4}$.  **A**

   A. $-16m - 22n$

   B. $16m - 22n$

   C. $16m + 22n$

   D. $-256m - 352n$

8. Evaluate $\sqrt{a^2 + b^2}$ for $a = 5$ and $b = 5$. Round to the nearest tenth if the result is not a whole number.  **D**

   A. 25

   B. 5

   C. 0

   D. 7.1

9. What is the solution of $77 = 103 - y$?  **D**

   A. $-26$

   B. 1.3

   C. 33

   D. 26

10. What is the solution of $\frac{1}{3}z = 48 - 29$?  **D**

    A. 22

    B. 19

    C. $\frac{19}{3}$

    D. 57

11. What is the solution of $6(a - 4) - 5 = 7a + 8$?  **A**

    A. $-37$

    B. $-\frac{37}{13}$

    C. $-17$

    D. 19

12. Solve $G = \frac{5h - 2}{3}$ for $h$.  **A**

    A. $h = \frac{3G + 2}{5}$

    B. $h = \frac{3G - 2}{5}$

    C. $h = \frac{3}{5}(G + 2)$

    D. $h = 5(3G + 2)$

**13.** What is the solution of $\frac{3}{c+3} = \frac{27}{63}$?  **D**

  **A.** 63

  **B.** 3

  **C.** 7

  **D.** 4

**14.** 34% of what number is 884?  **C**

  **A.** 300.56

  **B.** 918

  **C.** 2600

  **D.** 30,056

**15.** In 1985, a movie ticket cost $4.50. In 1994, a movie ticket sold for $7.65. What was the percent of increase over the original price?  **B**

  **A.** 59%

  **B.** 70%

  **C.** 41%

  **D.** 17%

**16.** A health food store owner has 20 pounds of granola that sells for $4.60 per pound. How many pounds of raisins selling for $2.50 per pound should she add to have a mixture that sells for $3.40 per pound?  **A**

  **A.** $26\frac{2}{3}$ pounds

  **B.** 16 pounds

  **C.** 80 pounds

  **D.** 4 pounds

**17.** What is the domain of the relation $\{(3, 4), (6, 7), (5, 5), (3, 2), (-1, 7), (5, 0)\}$?  **B**

  **A.** $\{-1, 0, 2, 3, 5, 6, 7\}$

  **B.** $\{-1, 3, 5, 6\}$

  **C.** $\{0, 2, 4, 5, 7\}$

  **D.** $\{3, 5, 7\}$

**18.** Which of the following relations is a function?  **A**

  **A.** $\{(-3, 4), (5, 7), (3, 4)\}$

  **B.** $\{(5, 2), (0, -2), (4, 1), (0, 3)\}$

  **C.** $2x^2 + y^2 = 10$

  **D.** None of these relations are functions.

**19.** What is the $x$-intercept of the graph of $5x - y = -85$?  **C**

  **A.** 17

  **B.** $-80$

  **C.** $-17$

  **D.** $-85$

**20.** Which equation has a graph that is a horizontal line?  **D**

  **A.** $3x + 2y = 2$

  **B.** $6x + 7 = 9$

  **C.** $xy = 1$

  **D.** $4y - 10 = 3$

**21.** Find an equation of the line that passes through $(-4, 1)$ and $(5, -2)$.  **C**

  **A.** $x + y = 3$

  **B.** $3x + y = -11$

  **C.** $x + 3y = -1$

  **D.** $x + 3y = -7$

**22.** Which line at the right has a slope of $-\frac{1}{4}$ and contains the point $(4, 2)$?  **B**

  **A.** $k$

  **B.** $l$

  **C.** $m$

  **D.** $n$

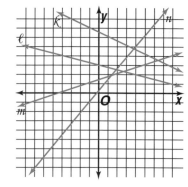

**23.** Which of the following equations has a graph that is parallel to the graph of $7x + 2y = 6$?  **C**

  **A.** $y = \frac{2}{7}x + 3$

  **B.** $y = -7x - 4$

  **C.** $y = -\frac{7}{2}x + 5$

  **D.** $y = \frac{7}{2}x + 3$

**24.** What are the coordinates of the midpoint of the segment whose endpoints are $(-3, -5)$ and $(-9, 5)$?  **B**

  **A.** $(-6, -10)$

  **B.** $(-6, 0)$

  **C.** $(-3, 10)$

  **D.** $(-3, 5)$

## Page B7  Review Lesson 1–4

**2a.**

| Stem | Leaf |
|------|------|
| 2 | 6 |
| 3 | 9 |
| 4 |  |
| 5 | 2 5 8 |
| 6 | 4 4 |
| 7 | 2 8 9 |

$5|2 = \$52$

## Page B9  Review Lesson 1–6

**13.**  $70 \div 10 + 3(6 - 3 \cdot 2) - 6 \div 2$

$= 70 \div 10 + 3(6 - 6) - 6 \div 2$    *substitution* $(=)$

$= 70 \div 10 + 3(0) - 6 \div 2$    *substitution* $(=)$

$= 70 \div 10 + 0 - 6 \div 2$    *mult. prop. of 0*

$= 7 + 0 - 3$    *substitution* $(=)$

$= 7 - 3$    *add. ident.*

$= 4$    *substitution* $(=)$

**14.**  $8(7 - 6) + 48 \div 4^2$

$= 8(1) + 48 \div 4^2$    *substitution* $(=)$

$= 8(1) + 48 \div 16$    *substitution* $(=)$

$= 8 + 48 \div 16$    *mult. ident.*

$= 8 + 3$    *substitution* $(=)$

$= 11$    *substitution* $(=)$

## Page B12  Review Lesson 1–9

**2.**

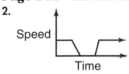

**3.**

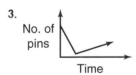

## Page B13  Chapter 1 Test

**19.**

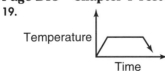

## Page B14  Review Lesson 2–1

**7.**

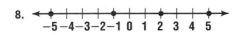

**8.**

**9.**

## Page B15  Review Lesson 2–2

**1a.**

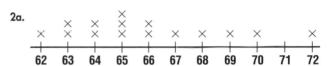

**2a.**

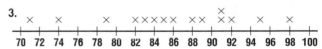

## Page B22  Review Lesson 2–9

**6.** Let $x =$ one number, then $x - 65 =$ the other number; $x + (x - 65) = 192$.  **7.** Let $x =$ the number of paperbacks, then $\frac{1}{3}x + 10 =$ the number of hardbacks; $x + \frac{1}{3}x + 10 = 90$.

## Page B23  Chapter 2 Test

**1.**

**3.**

## Page B41  Review Lesson 5–1

**1–6.**

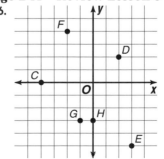

## Page B42  Review Lesson 5–2

**4.** $\{(3, -1), (5, 4), (7, 2)\}$; D $= \{3, 5, 7\}$; R $= \{-1, 4, 2\}$; I $= \{(-1, 3), (4, 5), (2, 7)\}$  **5.** $\{(-1, 6), (3, 0), (2, 4), (8, 0)\}$; D $= \{-1, 3, 2, 8\}$; R $= \{0, 4, 6\}$; I $= \{(6, -1), (0, 3), (4, 2), (0, 8)\}$

**6b.**

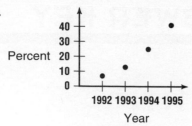

**9.**

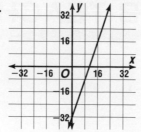

**Page B44   Review Lesson 5–4**

**4.**

**5.**

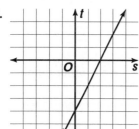

**6.**

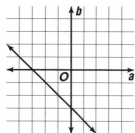

**7.**

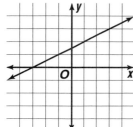

**8.**

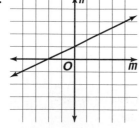

**10a.**

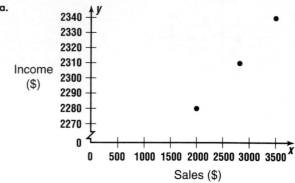

Sales ($)

**Page B45   Review Lesson 5–5**

**16a.**

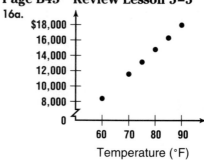

Temperature (°F)

**Page B48   Chapter 5 Test**

**3.**

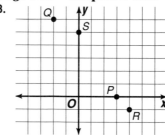

**9.**

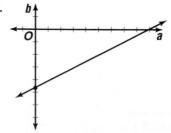

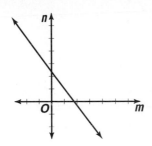

**11.**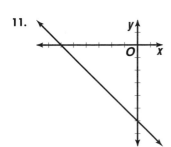

**Page B51  Review Lesson 6–3**

**1a.**
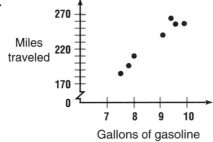

**2a.**
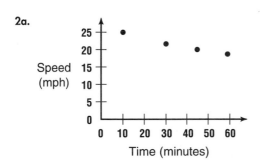

**3a.**
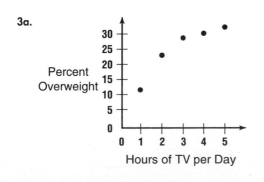

**Page B53  Review Lesson 6–5**

**1.**

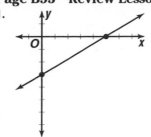

**2.**
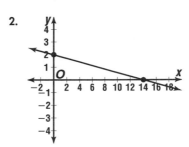

**3.**
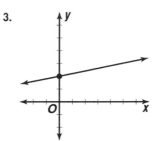

**4.**
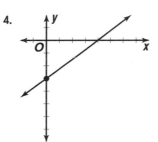

**5a.**
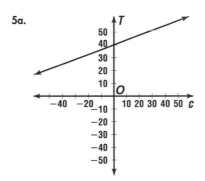

**Page B55  Review Lesson 6–7**

**16b.**
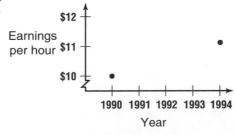

**7.**

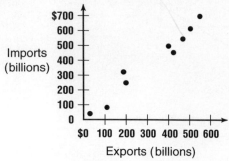

**12.**

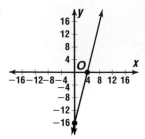

**13.**

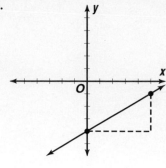